Funny Blood

Juliet Batten

Quacks Books

Q

ISBN 978-904446-37-8

British Library Cataloguing in Publication Data
Juliet Batten 2011
Funny Blood

Printed in 11 point Calibri
and published by
Quacks Books
Petergate
York YO1 7HU

This book is dedicated
to my daughter's
Manx Mum
with love

Acknowledgements

I would like to thank very much all those who helped and supported me through those difficult years of hospital visits and bleeds and all that happened with Ros as she grew up. They are part of my story. Particular thanks must go to Christine Tomkinson and Veronica Correa, who took on, often at very short notice, extra care of both my children and have been kind and loving friends all along. Thanks too, to extended family and friends further afield who were available on the phone at all times and supported and encouraged me.

Special thanks for help in writing this book go to: my niece, Bryony Evens for her suggestions, encouragement and for reading the early text; the late Alex Susman Shaw for her introduction and for her help and friendship throughout the years; Dr David Evans who provided information about the developments at Pendlebury and to both of them for all the information about von Willebrands; the late John Wyatt for allowing me to write about the late Grace Wyatt and Charnwood; staff at the Haemophilia Centre at Pendlebury and Cheadle Hulme School for allowing me to revisit; Graham Whitehead, Anna Hinchcliffe-Wood and Chris James at the Haemophilia Society for reading and commenting on various versions of the script; Manchester Evening News for permission to use articles and photo on pages 120 and 121; Woman's Own for permission to use photo on page 123; Ruth Rendell for reading the book so quickly and for her positive comments; my sister-in-law, Ann Evens, for her thoughtful and sometimes challenging encouragement and for proof reading the whole thing; Paul, for putting up with so much hassle throughout his early years; John, for his enormous patience and tolerance while helping me with many technicalities; Adrian, for the special part he now plays in our family.

Finally, heartfelt thanks to Ros, who scrutinised every word for me in the telling of her story and gave her loving commitment to the whole project.

Introduction

"What is the bleeding time?" So asked Sir Lancelot Spratt of a medical student in the film *Doctor In The House* from the book by Richard Gordon. He was not referring to the chronological time but to the time it takes for the blood to stop flowing from a deliberate cut in the skin, as part of specific tests to look at the mechanism of blood clotting - the subject of this book.

One of the better known but still rare blood clotting disorders is haemophilia, which manifests in the male because of its sex linked genetics. So, to be a female with a severe bleeding disorder is a rarity indeed and Ros is such a person. She has a condition called von Willebrands disorder Type III, which is a bleeding/clotting disorder classified into different types that manifests in varying ways. Type III is the most severe. It has similarities to severe haemophilia but with greater emphasis on bleeding from the nose and mouth; and severe menstrual bleeding in females, because the 'bleeding time' is abnormally long.

As Ros's mum writes, there are many positive times as well as all the negative ones throughout this account and she reflects on family life and the many problems that this bleeding disorder throws at them. The treatments themselves had major side effects – infections such as hepatitis B and C, and the worry of possible variant CJD from the plasma-derived blood products, which are the only method of treating this type of von Willebrands. Ros learnt how to give herself intravenous injections at home, no mean feat.

Bleeding disorders in females are only now being recognised and accepted by the medical profession in general, due to a group aptly named 'Women Bleed Too'. This is a focus group within the Haemophilia Society (a charity established in 1950 for males by males). It has been set up by women who have abnormal bleeding, to help with the recognition that they need as much help and support as do men with haemophilia.

This book follows the life of Ros, whom I have known and helped to care for since she was very small. Adopted by a warm and loving couple who had no inkling of Ros's problem, the book describes a child growing up into adult life, through all the trials and tribulations of normal development and teenage years. Battling with a frequently debilitating bleeding disorder but with such equanimity and aplomb, acceptance and quietude, dealing with pain, distress, despair and anger, along with much laughter and fun, made the family determined that Ros should lead as normal a life as possible. Ros's parents adopted another young child, Paul, who also had to adapt and accept the family trips to hospital when Ros needed medical intervention. I am sure this book will give insight, moral support and help for parents in a similar position to John and Juliet and that it will be an eye opener for those who are not!

Written by Alex Susman-Shaw, formerly Clinical Nurse Specialist (Haematology) Pendlebury Children's Hospital, Manchester, former vice chair and trustee of the Haemophilia Society, chair of north west group Haemophilia Society, in 2006.

Sadly, Alex died in 2009.

Prologue

On a beautiful sunny autumn day Ros and Adrian were married in a small country church in Worcestershire. It was a most lovely occasion and my heart was full of joy. My daughter's wish was coming true at last. With their families and friends around them Ros and Adrian made their vows during a service which included ten minutes of silent Quaker worship.

I felt strongly that I wanted to speak. This is what I said:

"I'd like to say a very special thank you today, to someone who isn't here at all and who does not even know what we are doing today, and that is Rosamund's mother – Rosamund's mother, who bore her and let her go and let her come to us, to care for and bring up. I'm so grateful to that lady, who I've never met, for giving me such a lovely daughter. I'm so proud of Ros today and I'm so proud of Adrian, and I wish them a long and happy life."

Chapter One

It was June 1974. I was on my way to meet my new daughter. I was nervous, thrilled and excited all at once, awash with apprehension, with a tight knot in my stomach. This day was to change my life for ever, in a way I could never have imagined. At last I was to become a mother. I would hold my baby in my arms.

The pen portrait given of this twelve-week old baby described her as a "petite little girl, who has quite a lot of light brown hair in which there are auburn tints. She is fair-skinned with light blue eyes. She is very responsive, having a ready smile for everyone". What more could a new parent want? She sounded perfect.

On this sunny day my husband, John, and I were driving to Frodsham in Cheshire, to the nursery where our prospective daughter was waiting for us. We were heading for Springfield Nursery at Newton Hall, part of the old 'cottage homes' managed by the National Children's Home (NCH), where many children in care lived in the seventies. Set on the outskirts of the town at the top of a hill there were splendid views across fields as we approached.

We drove in and parked outside Springfield Nursery. Near the door stood a pram. We passed it without a second glance and rang the bell. Matron welcomed us warmly and ushered us into a small room. After a short preliminary chat she said, "I'll just go and get her, she is in the pram outside". We had walked straight past her. Matron was only gone for a minute before she returned, holding the sweetest little baby in her arms.

"This is Mary," she said and handed her straight to me. She was lovely. She was fair-skinned, had light brown, wispy baby hair and was dressed in a little pink dress. I was enchanted. I held her, awkwardly at first; it was a while since I had handled such a small baby. She was warm and soft – was she really going to be ours? A plethora of thoughts and emotions ran through my head. On the one hand I felt euphoric at the possibility of possessing this lovely child, on the other uncertain at this very unusual situation. Despite all the social worker's visits and talks, the gathering together of baby equipment and the waiting, nothing could have prepared us for this moment.

Mary was happy for me to hold her. We looked at each other, introduced ourselves and smiled a lot. She was just as described in the pen portrait only even more beautiful. She seemed pleased to meet these new people who were about to pop her in the car and take her away to a strange house in Stockport. After a few minutes Matron said, "I'll leave you alone with her for a while," and disappeared.

I was so longing to have a baby of my own. We had spent agonising months and years trying to conceive. Each time we failed I was cross, angry and hurt. Once I threw a book across the lounge. It was called *The Peaceable Kingdom* but I did not feel very peaceful. I stopped going out when the schoolchildren were due out, as I did not want to see happy mothers and children if I could not be part of that scene. Now, while I sat with this smiling responsive baby in my arms, all those awful thoughts dropped away. The doubts and uncertainties began to recede. At last I could have a baby to care for, to love and bring up to adulthood. I would just be normal, push a pram and have people smile and chat when they saw my baby. I would not be left out and alone any more. It was the strangest feeling being here, but not giving birth. It was love at first sight for all of us. We both held her, played with her and talked to her and of course we talked to each other.

"Is this the baby we want?"

"Yes, but doesn't it feel strange?"

"We can't just walk out of here with her."

"It seems a very odd thing to do".

All these thoughts and more were running through our minds as we sat holding our first child.

John and I married in 1969 and moved to Stockport in 1970. After trying unsuccessfully to start a family, and after various tests and treatments for infertility, we had decided to try and adopt a baby. I knew from my work in children's homes that many babies and children needed new families. We had written to a large number of adoption agencies both locally and nationally, but most of them sent letters back saying that they were very sorry but their waiting lists were closed. However the NCH had accepted us on to their list after a long and rigorous application procedure, which had been carried out by a social worker from their head office in London. From November 1973 we had to be ready to accept a baby if one became available. This involved my stopping any work I was doing in order to care full-time for the baby, which seemed perfectly acceptable to me. I had a part-time job in the local playgroup, run in the church hall near our house, and John worked full-time as a lecturer at Stockport College. We prepared a nursery bedroom and bought a lot of the baby equipment we would need. It was quite hard to plan ahead when we did not know when our baby would arrive.

A few months before meeting Mary, the adoption agency had written to introduce us to a little boy, but we had decided not to follow up this introduction as he was of mixed race parentage. It was a hard decision to make, as we were keen to adopt quickly. Looking back now I am sometimes overwhelmed by the fact that if we had adopted the little boy we would never have met our lovely daughter and enjoyed getting to know her. Thirty years on I am so thankful to have known and helped her throughout her childhood and to see her now in adult life. She is a huge example to me and an inspiration to many, with her calm approach to life and particularly to all her problems.

The momentous day we met was a Tuesday. We had been told about Mary only the previous Friday so had only a few days to get ready for a baby! Essential shopping and cleaning was all there was really time for. We had been advised to bring with us a carrycot, an outdoor outfit, a shawl or blanket, nappies, feeding bottle and vacuum flask as well as a jug large enough to stand a bottle in to reheat a feed. A tiny teddy bear was popped in too.

Back came the Matron. "How are we doing?" she asked, or words to that effect. "Are you ready to take Mary home with you?"

"Yes," we said, but our reply was hesitant.

"Have you some reservations?" asked Matron.

"No", we replied, "but it just seems very strange that we can pick up this little baby and take her away with us, just like that."

Matron laughed and agreed that it must feel strange to us, but she reassured us that it was perfectly in order. We had a final briefing on Mary's routine, feeding times and general care and then it was time to set off for home. Gently and carefully I placed Mary in the carrycot on the back seat of our Mini, with the tiny teddy for company. Matron assured us once more that all was well and told us to phone her if we had any queries, and we said goodbye.

Mary was wide awake for the hour long journey home. Every few minutes I looked over my shoulder to check on her. Both John and I felt really strange. We had a real live baby in the back of our car and she was ours, or would be ours, once the formalities of adoption had been completed.

That night, we changed Mary's name. We had been advised that this was quite all right to do, but I felt we could not just abandon the person she already was. We had been going through a list of boys' and girls' names and had a shortlist for each. We decided that Rosamund, our preferred name, would fit very well in front of Mary. When she was older and knew of her origins she could always drop the Rosamund and revert to her original name if she so wished.

Our first week at home with Ros was very exciting and very tiring. We were coping with the emotional reactions associated with adoption, while at the same time adjusting our lives to incorporate this tiny baby. I was on a high, phoning family and friends to tell them our good news, but was not concentrating well on the job in hand. The bottle feeds I made up were lumpy and the teats clogged up constantly, disrupting feeding times, which were ideal times for bonding with a new baby. Fortunately for me, my mother, Dorothy Evens, came to stay for a week to help out. She was thrilled to have another grandchild and was a tower of strength during those first few days. Things began to settle down after my brother, Nicholas, a psychologist, suggested in a phone call that a routine for each day might be a good thing. His calm instructions about making up all the bottle feeds for the day and his timely advice helped me to settle down.

Ros was such a good baby and seemed to have no adverse reactions to coming to us, but I was very tired during those first weeks and experiencing emotional setbacks. One in particular springs to mind. The adoption agency had assured us that we would soon have visits from the local social services department and from the health visitor, but no one came in these first two weeks. As there was a weekly baby clinic close by, I took Ros to be weighed one afternoon in the second week. The health visitor referral had not been passed to the staff there, so no one knew me. I immediately burst into tears and explained that we had just adopted Ros. When the nurse had weighed her and found she was gaining weight, I was reassured. But the incident left me feeling strangely isolated and I was to feel this isolation much more in the years ahead.

Ros settled in and her development progressed well. We were getting used to being a family and were entertaining family members and friends who came visiting to welcome her. I wheeled her out in her posh new pram. Many friends and acquaintances, when they saw her, remarked, "Isn't she like her Daddy!"

Ros in her posh new pram

The local social services duly appointed a guardian *ad litem* to see us through the court procedures. This social worker and the NCH social worker visited us regularly for the next few months.

Before we could apply to the court to adopt Ros, she had to undergo a blood test, the W R and Kahn test, which we understood was to check for any signs of venereal disease. This was a routine test in those days and was done at Withington Hospital in Manchester, a short car drive away. An appointment for this was made, and we duly reported to this hospital's pathology laboratory. Ros was very good while the blood was taken and only cried when the needle was actually stuck into her heel. Afterwards her heel bled profusely. As we came out of the hospital entrance we stopped on a seat while I searched in my bag for some tissues. Opposite us an ambulance was parked. The driver watched as we cleaned up Ros's foot and offered us a large pad of gauze to put under it. We thanked him for this kind action, as the bleeding continued and only stopped by the time we reached home. We thought no more about it until the next day when, as I was changing Ros ready for bed, I noticed that her leg and foot were covered in little red spots and bruise marks. My first thought was that she might have blood poisoning from the needle the previous day, though I had no idea how this would manifest itself. We phoned our local health centre and were told to bring Ros to see the doctor. It was our general practitioner's (GP's) partner who examined her foot and leg and reckoned that it was just bruising from the previous day. He asked if her leg had been squeezed rather hard, and together we assumed that this was the reason for the marks. We were reassured. Ros did not seem to be in pain and only yelled for her tea! The next day the bruises were still apparent, but Ros had no obvious discomfort. Very soon the bruises faded and all seemed well.

By September Ros was beginning to move about and could roll over from her back to her front. She developed a backward slide and began getting quite grubby on the floor. She was developing very normally and was a cheerful little baby, very interested in everything around her. The guardian *ad litem* continued her formal visits and could see that all was going well for our adoption application. We were so enjoying our new daughter.

October came and we went to the County Court hearing for our adoption application. It was a very brief ceremony; the judge said he was happy to sign the adoption order and wished us well for the future. We were out again before we had time to get comfy on our chairs. Ros was now our legally adopted daughter and it felt good.

We noticed that Ros developed a tiny crack in her gum where her first tooth was pushing through. Looking back now it seems strange that it did not bleed, as she later had immense trouble from gum bleeds. Perhaps there was a tiny bleed that we did not notice.

Soon after going to court I took Ros to our GP for her first round of vaccinations. She did cry when the needle went in, but had no further ill effects from this injection. She was becoming very active and could pull herself forward a little on her elbows as well as slide about backwards. During the appointment our GP commented on a small bruise on her forehead. I said that she was becoming more active and had recently 'crawled' against a piece of furniture and I distinctly remember saying, "I suppose babies bruise easily." His response was that babies did *not* bruise easily, and he recommended that we should take her for a blood test for further investigation. I was not unduly worried, even when he suggested that she might have a lifelong bleeding condition. He must however, have sown a seed in our minds because I realised some time later that his remarks had worked their way through my subconscious.

A week later Ros's leg was bruised and purple for no apparent reason and we were concerned to see this further bruising, which we now know as purpura (an eruption of small purple spots caused by extravastation of blood). Once again we visited the GP's surgery and again saw our doctor's partner, who reassured us there was nothing to worry about.

We soon received an appointment to attend our local hospital, Stepping Hill Hospital in Stockport, for the blood test and Ros and I reported to the pathology laboratory on the appointed day. Here we experienced our first bad time together. The technician asked me to perch on a high lab stool without any back support and hold Ros in my arms while he carried out the bleeding time test.

First he stuck a needle in Ros's earlobe, to instigate bleeding and

7

then collected each drop of blood as it welled up, on to a round filter paper. When the paper was full a new one was started. Ros yelled the whole time and this upset me too. He continued this procedure for *45 minutes,* and then said that there was obviously some abnormality, which had been apparent to him after 20 minutes. Why he had continued for a further 25 minutes seeing our distress I do not know. More blood was taken for testing and we came away. I was thoroughly devastated by the experience.

A week later we had to return to the hospital for a further blood sample to be taken as the results from the first blood taken were inconclusive. Stepping Hill then referred us to the Royal Manchester Children's Hospital at Pendlebury, Salford, for further tests.

After this alarming experience we were very glad when Christmas came and we drove south to be with both sets of grandparents. Over the festive season Ros was thoroughly spoiled, enjoyed all the extra attention and cut her second tooth.

Our appointment for Pendlebury came early in the New Year and on the Sunday prior to it we all drove to Salford to find the way to the children's hospital, as I was apprehensive about going on my own. Tuesday was a full teaching day for John so he could not come with us. We did not know then that after a few more visits the car would start finding its own way to this hospital.

Pendlebury Hospital had opened in 1873 and was by now showing its age. The yellow brick Victorian main building, with its impressive colonnade and steps at the front, very grand in its heyday, now looked generally dilapidated and dirty. Later extensions built on only heightened this air of shabbiness and ageing, as did the newer red brick buildings dotted around the grounds. When we arrived for our appointment we had to find our way to the pathology laboratory. This was housed near the admissions unit and was down some dingy steps in a department at lower ground level.

We had to wait an hour before we saw the specialist. We sat in a small corridor, opposite the entrance to the laboratories. All children who were outpatients had to report here. There was a very disheartening atmosphere and the waiting space was barely adequate for mothers and children. When our turn came we had

8

to walk through the laboratory working area to reach the tiny office where the consultation was carried out.

The specialist we saw was Dr Evans, a consultant paediatrician, who specialised in pathology and haematology. He was a tall, angular man with glasses. He seemed to be very knowledgeable, for which I was thankful, but I can remember nothing of any discussions we had. There was no nurse on hand to help with the appointment. Dr Evans was working on his own. Further blood for testing was taken from Ros's tiny veins and we were asked to return to the hospital in two weeks for the results.

During the next fortnight I noticed that Ros's arms were fairly bruised from her crawling sessions. She was still dragging herself along on her arms, so they were getting some rough treatment from her. Otherwise the days went by very normally and routinely, until the day came for our second appointment. Again, it was a Tuesday so John could not go with us and again we reported to the dingy, unwelcoming path lab and saw Dr Evans in his tiny laboratory. I was tense, wondering what the test results were going to show. Surely my beautiful new baby had nothing seriously wrong with her? I had a sinking feeling that it might be bad news.

Letters of welcome from members of the family

Friday -

Dear Juliet, John & Rosamund,

We're all delighted to hear of the 3 of you and wish you great happiness together. All the best for the settling down days — they can be hectic enough for anyone but even more so for an instant family, I should think. R. Mum will be a tower of strength — as we know only too well — do make the most of all the extra help, says Aunty Anne!

Dear John, Juliet and Rosamund Mary,

Hi, and welcome. Congratulations. Jolly good show etc. I expect it must be more exciting having it happen all suddenly like that.

What with a new baby and tropical fish and all I shall obviously have to come and see you soon. All the best,

Geoffrey.

P.S. I think I'll start a sweep on the time it takes for someone to come up to you in the street and say: "Isn't she like her mother?"

10

Chapter Two

With Ros on my knee I sat in that dingy room and tried to understand what Dr Evans was saying. I'm sure it was not easy for him, and that he was as cheerful as he could be, having to impart bad news, but on this occasion I disliked him. As he talked, he looked over the top of his spectacles, so that I rarely had eye contact with him, which made me feel uneasy. I felt even more unsettled when he told me that Ros had something called von Willebrand's disease.

He explained that this disease was rather like haemophilia, a rare blood clotting disorder, but that it was not nearly as bad. She would, he said, have it for the rest of her life. Her blood carried only 3% of the clotting factor needed, factor VIII, which meant that she was severely affected with this disease. Above 50-60% of clotting factor could be considered a safe percentage; under that, bleeding problems would occur. He told me that her platelets carried an abnormality too. They did not have the sticky, glue-like substance required to form the plug for the clotting mechanism. She would continue to bruise and bleed easily, as she had already done. He advised that we should bring her to see him if she got bad bruises or bumps.

I could not take this all in at once. I was shocked, too shocked to ask any intelligent questions. I did not have any special reactions but I can remember wondering how I was going to tell John, who would be home late after his evening lectures. He did not like to be disturbed at work, but I felt this diagnosis was important enough to warrant breaking into his busy day. When I phoned and asked to be put through to him he had to be called out of a lecture and was not pleased. Work was work and home was home, and the two should not meet. Was I to carry this burden on my own now and in the future? It seemed so at the time.

When John got home, however, and we talked some more, I was relieved to have someone to share the bad news with. Soon, of course, he was finding times when he could be free to sit with Ros at home, drive us to hospital or do whatever was needed.

I knew little or nothing about haemophilia. I had once read an article in a women's magazine about a boy who suffered from it and had decided that this was one handicap I would definitely not like to deal with. When I was about 17 years old my brother Nick had suggested that I might think about nursing as a career. I baulked at the idea as I did not like the sight of blood! I had kept an open mind about how I might cope with many other diseases or disabilities. Haemophilia seemed to be a very frightening disease. And now, here I was with an eight-month old daughter with a bleeding disorder very like haemophilia.

Thoughts began to rush into my head. How was I going to protect Ros from bruising and bleeding? She was becoming very active now, sitting up better each day and she had a new activity, which was to bounce down hard on to her knees in a crawling position.

The practical side of my nature took over after a few days. First, old socks were turned into 'extra protection' pads for her knees and elbows, with the hope that they might reduce the bruises. Next I was down at the local market in Stockport buying pieces of foam rubber to wrap around our furniture.

Life went on in our routine way – shopping, cleaning, cooking and playing with Ros, but watching her all the time and trying not to be too neurotic about her care. The health visitor came. She had never heard of von Willebrand's disease (vWd). Afterwards, I was cross with and critical of her for not being more supportive. That sense of isolation I had felt at the clinic was with me again. Then I had felt isolated by having an adopted baby; now I felt that I was the only one in the world with a child with this strange condition.

There was no one to talk to about vWd, apart from the hospital specialist, and even he had admitted that he had not had much experience of children with it. I felt that it was a clinical area of his work and that it was not his duty to help us through the more emotional and traumatic side of this problem. We did not have a sudden disaster on our hands, nor was it a life or death situation needing to be resolved. We were starting to cope with a condition for which we had very little information. We could only move forward with that small amount of knowledge, and hope to build on it as time went on, coping with particular situations as they arose. We could not foresee the problems. Ros did not change; she simply went on developing beautifully. I changed; I changed from a proud new mum with a perfect child into someone who could not understand what was happening. I was overcome by nagging doubts about haemophilia and its possible effects. Our extended families were helpful and gave much needed moral support and reassurance over the phone, but we were otherwise alone and worried.

When Ros was diagnosed, von Willebrand's (vWd) was classed as a rare disease. It was similar to haemophilia in that those affected would suffer prolonged bleeding, but it could be diagnosed in both men and women, whereas haemophilia mainly affects men. The condition was first described by Dr Erik von Willebrand, a Finnish physician, in the 1920's. He had been studying an extended family in the Aland Islands, which lie between Sweden and Finland in the Baltic. Many members of this family were experiencing severe bleeding. His conclusions were that the problem was not true haemophilia as many of those affected were females, so he termed it 'pseudo-haemophilia'. After further study he recognised that the blood platelets were dysfunctional. Later the protein involved was identified and the disorder was then named after Dr von Willebrand. The major symptoms of this disease are:

- easy bruising
- frequent or prolonged nose bleeds
- frequent or prolonged menstrual bleeding
- prolonged bleeding following childbirth, surgery or dental work
- bleeding from the mucous membrane/soft tissue areas.

Accurate diagnosis of vWd can be difficult. One of the problems is that the vWd factor can be temporarily raised under certain conditions. Stress or anxiety, for example, the distress of a child at the time of the blood test, actually raises the levels of adrenalin and subsequently stimulates the body to release vWd factor. To have an accurate result, the test may have to be repeated several times. Another problem with diagnosis of young girls who present with bleeding problems is that they may be confused with carriers of haemophilia. Haemophilia is passed down through the female line, but the levels of clotting factor for carriers are not normally as low as in vWd.

We had sent regular reports to the adoption agency as to Ros's progress and informed them of this health problem. Dr Evans had also written to them, as he was anxious to know the family history, von Willebrand's being an inherited disorder. Checks were made by social workers and doctors relevant to Ros's birth and adoption but there was no record of any vWd in either of her natural parents. It had to be assumed that Ros had acquired it through spontaneous mutation of the gene involved.

The agency was concerned for us and had checked with their doctor about this disease. They tried to be reassuring and said in a letter, *Apparently it is a very rare disease, but nothing at all as serious as haemophilia, so we hope it is not going to be too restricting for Rosamund.* This helped us to continue to think of the vWd as 'rare', but mild as compared to haemophilia and not too much to worry about.

But I did worry about it. Caring for Ros began to be a constant source of anxiety for me. My bonding with this very special baby was going well. It was easy to love Ros right from the start. She was loving and responsive, smiled and 'talked' and enjoyed playing games. Now the need to be a really good mother came over me. I had all this extra responsibility to keep her safe. My natural mothering instincts were coming into play and Ros seemed to have accepted both John and me as her parents. Finding the strength to cope with the extra and very real necessities of her condition was coming from deep inside me. The extra physical energy required was always there.

Ros was beginning to pull herself up to a standing position. She started going through a period of having lots of falls and bumps, inevitable for any small child as he or she starts to get mobile, but particularly hazardous for a child with Ros's condition. One day she pulled the kitchen chair down on top of herself and got a nasty knock on the forehead. Although the old sock 'protectors' on her arms and legs were helping a bit, she still managed to get big bruises on her arms. It was becoming harder and harder for us as we tried to protect her from serious hurt. Our beautiful fair- skinned baby began to have ugly black bruises appearing on her tiny body.

Juliet, John and Ros, November 1974

Our attendance at Dr Evans's haemophilia clinic at Pendlebury was every four months and was vital for our care of Ros. We slowly began to find out more about vWd. Although the clinic was held in the far from satisfactory conditions in the path lab, we appreciated much later that Dr Evans was a pioneer in the field of haemophilia care. Haemophilia centres in the United Kingdom were being set up in the 1950's at the request of the Haemophilia Society, which itself was only founded in 1950. These haemophilia centres mainly developed in hospitals with reasonably sophisticated laboratory facilities, so that the necessary blood tests could be carried out more effectively and a proper diagnosis made. The majority of people in charge of these laboratories did not have the expertise, or possibly the interest, to run a full clinical service for the haemophilia patients. As time went by they were replaced by haematologists, who were trained in both the laboratory and clinical aspects of blood diseases.

Dr Evans had visited Great Ormond Street Hospital in London and some of the larger hospitals in the USA, to see how they managed.

These visits had influenced him profoundly. He had been appointed as a pathologist to Pendlebury in the 1960's and after a couple of years he knew that he wanted to look more fully at children with all blood disorders, including leukaemia. He asked his colleagues at Pendlebury if he could have facilities for a haematology out-patients clinic. The senior paediatrician said that if he had a clinic he would need some beds too, so Dr Evans became the first haematologist in the region to have beds. He was also consultant pathologist to two other hospitals in the Manchester area, Booth Hall and Monsall, and each of these had various laboratories, including haematology. It soon became apparent that the more complicated cases went to Pendlebury. The clinic there would be the main base; there were a greater number of specialists and a professor of paediatrics on hand.

We gradually began to absorb more information about vWd, and could retain it, which was important. There was no handy guide to the condition, but we were given a list of the haemophilia centres around the country, where Ros could be treated if we were away from home. We were also given a very small 'Green Card' which looked scary to me. On the front it said, *Notes on the Care of Patients with Hereditary Haemorrhagic Disorders.* It stated that Ros had a special medical condition and the card must be shown if we went anywhere for help or treatment. Ros must never be given aspirin and she had to have her immunisations subcutaneously to avoid the possibility of a bleed.

At one of our visits to Pendlebury we saw one of Dr Evans's assistants. At the end of the consultation I asked him if he knew anyone we could talk to about Ros and he replied, "Oh, you want the Haemophilia Society", as if it was something I should have asked long ago. He gave me the name and telephone number of the secretary of the north west group, and that evening I phoned her and we talked for nearly an hour. She had a son with haemophilia, but knew nothing about girls being bleeders. She was, however, most sympathetic and told me about the local haemophilia group and its activities. I was so glad to talk to someone who understood a little of what we were going through and of our worries and fears for the future.

It was through this group that we gradually met other parents of boys with haemophilia. Some of them had harrowing stories to tell about the way they had been treated by the authorities, before their children had been diagnosed. Most young boys with bruises had been removed from their parents for 48 hours while investigations were carried out as to the cause of their injuries. How thankful we were that our GP had not given even a hint of concern about possible abuse. For a GP in the 1970's he was unusually well informed about bleeding disorders.

We had been advised to take Ros to the hospital if we thought a bump or bruise needed treatment, but the criterion for measuring this was unknown to us. However, very soon the day came when we were put to our first test. A colleague of John's from Stockport College had made a little red trolley for Ros with her name on it. It was just the right size for her to pull herself up and take a few steps pushing it. One evening at teatime she managed to fall into it, on to some wooden bricks. A large lump formed on her forehead. A phone call to Pendlebury confirmed our suspicions that they would want to see her. John took her as we were expecting a friend to come for a meal. On this occasion treatment was not needed, but the lump was black and blue and looked horrid for some days.

A few weeks later came another scare. This time it was bleeding from Ros's gum, where a new tooth was pushing through. It had been oozing now and then for some days. One day the bleeding persisted, so off we went to Pendlebury. This time Ros was given some medicine to take which would help to stop the bleeding. This was Epsikapron, an antifibrinolytic drug that stops the blood clot from breaking down too quickly. A few days later, we were back at the hospital one evening after Ros had bitten her tongue. The wound had oozed slowly all afternoon and showed no sign of stopping. This time, Ros was given her first injection of cryoprecipitate. Our knowledge of it was nil on this first occasion, but it had the desired effect and stopped the bleeding.

This cryoprecipitate, or cryo as it was usually known, was a crude form of clotting factor, made from human blood. It contained the necessary clotting factor VIII which Ros needed. It had been discovered in 1964, but in 1967, when Dr Evans started his work with children

17

with bleeding disorders, there was no cryo available for him to use.

Because treatments were primitive and varied, boys with haemophilia suffered a good deal of pain from their bleeds. Fred Bates, a friend we made later on, remembers some of the treatments that were given to him as a small boy. Gypsy remedies were recommended; one of them was to apply flour on cuts, without letting the flour get into the veins. For joint bleeds it was suggested that hot tea leaves, in gauze or an old towel, should be wrapped round the affected limb. One doctor told Fred's mum to give him a cigarette to smoke to help relieve pain. She did and it worked. Fred was seven years old! The nastiest treatment Fred could remember was a recipe that came from the USA and was on trial here. The recipe consisted of a pound of butter and a pound of peanuts, mixed together to a thick treacly consistency. Fred was given a spoonful of this daily. He found it very unpalatable. While he was on it, though, he had no bleeds; when he stopped taking it he had a bleed! Fred attended Booth Hall hospital, which was the children's hospital for east Manchester. They could only advise bed rest for joint bleeds. For mouth bleeding he was given cotton wool soaked in topical thrombin to suck. At the age of seven he transferred to Manchester Royal Infirmary for treatment.

Pendlebury started making cryo for their own use. Dr Evans ordered a large centrifuge and a huge vacuum flask. He persuaded the hospital authorities to buy some plastic bags for blood donations. Donors had to be encouraged to come to the hospital to give their blood. In London this had been easy, as the Red Cross kept a list of people who were prepared to give blood at the drop of a hat, but in Manchester no such arrangements existed. Dr Evans and his colleagues had to ask the Blood Transfusion Service (BTS) to find people who were prepared to donate blood, but they had no system for doing this. Furthermore, at that time the blood from the BTS came in bottles and the authorities could not see why they should have to pay for plastic bags, when bottles came for free. At that time, the head of the BTS had the job of providing blood for hospitals. It took a while before he agreed that his transfusion service should provide blood products, as services in other parts of the country were doing. When the BTS at last started to produce cryo, he refused to send the product to any of the other hospitals in the region. He told the doctors that they must send their patients to Pendlebury, to be treated by Dr Evans.

To produce cryo, the plasma was first spun off from the whole blood and then frozen at a specific temperature. Next it was slowly defrosted at another specific temperature and as it defrosted the substance that leached out was the precipitate. This precipitate could be frozen and stored ready for use.

Cryo being prepared for the injection looked a fairly primitive process. The packs of cryo were taken from the freezer and placed into a special water bath for defrosting. (My memory is that very often they used the sink in the room and ran the hot tap, but I am assured by talking with the staff who administered it in those days that they did use the water bath to heat the cryo to 38°C but that sometimes, yes, they did use the sink because it was quicker. The water bath was not always cleaned out and could harbour bacterial organisms, so actually warming the cryo up under running water was a safer method. Later, defrosting was done in dry-heat ovens). The cryo was drawn up into a syringe from the warmed packs. The amount used was calculated by the weight of the child. It was a slow and messy procedure.

In the 1970's the new factor concentrates were being developed. These freeze-dried products were more refined than cryo. There was much less interference in preparation, therefore they were much safer. These treatments were being administered to boys with haemophilia and were much easier to give. They revolutionised treatment for them, they were not given in such large volume and they opened the doors for home treatment. Home treatment was being carried out and evaluated in the 1970's.

But for Ros, with her slightly different condition, cryo was still the best treatment and continued to be so for many years. It was known that cryo contained large amounts of factor VIII and it was the vWd factor attached to the factor VIII that was so important and so necessary.

Some pages from the Green Card – the only information we had

Reasons for Treatment at the Haemophilia Centre

1. Bleeding into a joint shown by pain or swelling. No attempt should be made to move a painful joint.

2. Bleeding into a muscle.

3. Injury to the neck, mouth, tongue, face or eye.

4. Severe knocks on the head and un-usual headache.

5. Heavy or persistent bleeding from any site.

6. Severe pain (particularly abdominal pain) or swelling in any site.

7. All open wounds requiring stitching.

Patients should know the procedure for obtaining treatment at or admission to the Haemophilia Centre at which they are registered. This procedure may vary from one district to another. In many areas it may be possible for the patient to phone directly to the Ambulance Service and have the ambulance take him to the Haemophilia Centre. Arrange-ments for admission should be discussed with the specialist at the Haemophilia Centre.

Small Cuts Not Requiring Stitching

Strangely enough, small cuts are seldom very troublesome and can be treated in the usual way, with careful gentle washing and the application of a 'non-stick' or absorbable clean dressing soaked in Stypven, or other suitable local haemostatic, which can be supplied to the patients by the Haemophilia Centre.

Bruises which are visibly black and blue are also not usually dangerous, except in certain situations such as the scalp or neck. The full development of serious bleeding after injury in haemophiliacs is usually delayed for 2-3 hours, so that there is nearly always time for the patient to reach a Haemophilia Centre.

3

4

Drugs and Immunisation

The haemophiliac should not take Aspirin in any form since it may increase his tendency to bleed. The name Aspirin (acetylsalicylic acid) may not be clearly displayed on packets and labels. If, after scrutinising the label carefully the haemo-philiac is uncertain as to whether or not a preparation contains aspirin he should ask the chemist.

Preparations which do not contain aspirin and can safely be used are:–

Paracetamol (Panadol)
Codeine Phosphate
Dihydrocodeine (D. F. 118)
Mefenamic Acid (Ponstan)

Patients should not receive any intra-muscular injection.

Immunisation by intradermal or sub-cutaneous injection and vaccination on the other hand are usually quite safe, but the sites should be inspected daily and if there is any worry about the degree of reaction the Haemophilia Centre should be consulted.

Care of Teeth

Haemophiliacs should take particular care of their teeth and receive regular dental treatment to avoid the necessity of extractions. Fillings are usually quite safe, but it is advisable not to have local anaesthetics by injection unless anti-haemophilic replacement therapy is given beforehand at a Haemophilia Centre, as these injections can cause dangerous swelling. If extractions are required they should be undertaken in a hospital which has a Haemophilia Centre where treatment with infusions of plasma or concentrates will be given to prevent bleeding.

Any difficulty in obtaining dental care should be discussed with the specialists at the Haemophilia Centre.

5

6

20

Chapter Three

Real problems started for us when Ros began to walk. Crawling had not been too hazardous for her, but with the development of walking skills she could really take off. Now, while I turned my back for a minute, she could go further and more quickly and be exploring something new.

It was on the Batten grandparents' level back lawn that Ros took her first few steps unaided, with the help and encouragement of my mother. She practised this new art all the time, everywhere, while we held our breath, but it was good to see her getting around independently, even with the inevitable falls and sudden 'sit downs'.

One of those comical 'sit downs' turned into a nightmare for us all. We were in the gardens at Tatton Park in Cheshire on a beautiful, hot, sunny day. It was here, by a bench, that

Ros learning to walk, with help from Grandma Evens

Ros decided to practise her walking. We watched as she solemnly tottered round the bench, holding on well, when suddenly down she went with a bump. She hit her chin on the seat as she went down and bit her tongue. Blood began oozing out fast and continuously. We rushed straight off to Pendlebury.

Although it was a Sunday, Ros was treated fairly promptly with cryo, but the doctor on call wanted to keep her in for observation. Of course we could not argue with this decision. Ros's health and well being were paramount, but this was the first time we had been confronted with an overnight stay. We had come unprepared for staying and Ros had no change of clothes, although the hospital could provide basics for her.

We were taken to Borchardt ward, a large ward where children with any blood problems were cared for. Borchardt was one of the six main wards of the hospital, designed on the Florence Nightingale principle, beds down each side and a wide central space and was named after one of the pioneering physicians of the early years at Pendlebury. Like the other five wards it was large, light and airy, with a high ceiling and big windows. There was much activity on the ward, children in bed or playing about, babies in high sided cots, families visiting and parents sitting by their sick children. While many of these children were suffering from leukaemia, the atmosphere on the ward nevertheless was relaxed and happy. We thought that Ros, being so young, would soon drop off to sleep, but her tongue was still oozing blood despite the treatment and it took several hours for her to settle. We crept away at last feeling awful at leaving her. Just before going to bed we phoned the hospital to hear that Ros was 'satisfactory', whatever that meant.

The next morning we phoned to check how she was and then drove to the hospital arriving around 9.00am. Ros looked awful; she was wearing a blood stained dress, was very pale and was still bleeding from her mouth. She was such a beautiful little baby it was awful to see the blood slowly oozing out of her. Poor little child, she was fretful and miserable at having been abandoned at this strange place by her parents. She had not had anything to eat. She managed to eat some food later in the day and was more cheerful after it. It was a long hot day and trying to keep Ros amused, but resting, was difficult. In the opposite bed to Ros was a little boy about the same age. I chatted with his mother and she told me what was wrong with him. It appeared that he was the opposite to Ros, his blood was too thick and clotted too easily. I told her about Ros's condition. We decided that an easy solution to both our children's problems would be to take blood from each of them, mix it up and re-inject it. If only it was that simple! How little I understood about bleeding and blood disorders.

Dr Evans wanted to keep Ros in hospital for a second night. Her bleeding was under control by evening, but a slight knock or bite could start it off again. With a heavy heart I left her for another night and went home full of nervous energy to make a meal and do some chores. It was horrible being at home without my lovely child, who should have been sleeping peacefully in her cot without a care in the world.

Back at the hospital by 8.00am the next morning I was pleased to see Ros looking chirpier. It was a relief to see her so much better. She had suffered no further bleeding overnight. I waited all morning for a decision on going home only to be told at midday that Ros's haemoglobin level was low and that she would need a blood transfusion, after which I could take her home. The transfusion was not set up till 3.30pm and only finally finished at 10.00pm. Ros had been more herself, though had not had much sleep. Trying to keep her calm and still while the blood transfusion went on was quite harrowing, so we were both exhausted by the time we reached home at 10.45pm. What with Ros's crying, my worrying and the summer heat, it had been quite a day.

Inevitably, we had to return to the hospital for a check up in the morning. Dr Evans reckoned that all was well, so we came away quickly before he changed his mind. I could not face another day of sitting in the hospital. We had a quiet, restorative day at home, although the weather was still very hot and humid. Ros was still rather dozy the next day, so I was careful to watch her every move.

There were two outcomes from these few traumatic days. One was the decision for me to stay at the hospital if Ros was admitted again. I could not bear leaving her there by herself and needed to find out quickly about staying overnight.

The era of not allowing parents anywhere near their children while they were in hospital had ended, mainly owing to an organisation called the National Association for the Welfare of Children in Hospital (NAWCH). In 1961 'Care for Children in Hospital' was set up, following the television showing of two films made by James Robertson, a psychotherapist, which demonstrated the levels of anxiety and stress experienced by young children in hospital when separated from their mothers. (*A Two Year Old goes to Hospital* 1953 and *Going to Hospital with Mother* 1953).

Parents had not previously been allowed to stay with their children as their presence was thought to be disruptive, and visiting times were short too. One mother, distressed by this situation, consulted James Robertson. He encouraged the formation of parent groups who would educate themselves and look at the key issues of parental access and unrestricted visiting. With the help of health professionals these groups grew and eventually formed a national body, changing the name from 'Care for Children in Hospital' to NAWCH in 1965. A government report in 1959, *The Platt Report, The Welfare of Children in Hospital*, had outlined recommendations on the non-medical aspects of care of hospitalised children, recognising their emotional needs as well as their physical needs and the importance of parental involvement during their stay in hospital. NAWCH was instrumental in getting the Platt Report adopted as official Ministry of Health policy. Nevertheless, hospitals were not legally obliged to carry out this policy. Fortunately for me, Pendlebury in 1975 was very encouraging to parents some ten years on from all this. I made some enquiries and found out that there was limited accommodation for parents and I was told how to book a place.

The other outcome was a much more practical one. I decided to pack an emergency bag, which I could grab if we had to disappear to the hospital suddenly. I bought a red shopping bag and filled it with a change of clothes, some nightwear and toiletries for both of us.

Some months passed then Ros tripped over the back step and bit her tongue again. We decided to have our tea before leaving for the hospital as the bleeding, though continuous, was slow. It was just as well as, after treating her, the doctor wanted her to stay in. I stayed too. The emergency bag came into its own. Ros's tongue continued to bleed slowly all night. The wound was further back on her tongue than the previous one so made her vomit, which kept breaking the clot. Ros got very tired and irritable during the next twenty-four hours and it was a long miserable night followed by a long miserable day for both of us. By the second morning the bleeding had stopped and Ros was more cheerful, especially after she had had some food. John came to sit with her while I went home for about four hours, taking relief from a pile of ironing, after the stress and trauma of the hospital. I came back to spend another night in the hospital accommodation. This was in another building, a short walk away from Borchardt ward. My memory of it is hazy now, but I know it offered very basic amenities and that a lot of the mothers smoked heavily. The view of the hospital mortuary across the yard did not cheer our spirits.

Two more long tedious days were spent helping Ros recover. She was allowed up at last and played happily, if shakily, in the playroom on the ward. Finally we were allowed to go home. Ros was very anaemic and had iron medicine to boost her haemoglobin. She looked very pale and for a while took to walking instead of her usual running, for which I was thankful. Her full energy was not restored for several days.

A teenage friend, Emma, and her mother Mary, an experienced nurse, came to babysit for us while we went to our first meeting of the north west group of the Haemophilia Society. This was held at St Mary's Hospital in Manchester. It was the first time John and I had been out together, leaving Ros in someone else's care. The meeting was interesting and informative. I was told about a book, *Journey* by Robert and Suzanne Massie, which we subsequently bought. It was a long and very harrowing story about bringing up their son, who was a haemophiliac, in America in the 1950's and 60's. I felt so glad that treatments had markedly improved since their day. Around the same time ITV's *World in Action* did a programme on haemophilia. We were building up a store of knowledge on the subject, but much of it was not relevant to Ros's condition. As far as we knew, other girl bleeders did not exist.

Dr Evans had set up an annual review clinic for his haemophilia patients. This was a good start to comprehensive care for these children, as he invited a dentist, joint specialist and physiotherapist to be in attendance, as well as nursing staff support. Dr Evans did not like the idea of his young patients having to make repeated trips to Manchester from, for example, Lancaster or Burnley, to see other consultants. The dentist was keen on preventative dentistry in children and needed no persuading to join this small team. The joint specialist had an interest in joint disease in children. The physiotherapist and nursing staff were always in attendance.

The review clinic was held in the outpatients department of

the children's hospital, an old building in Gartside Street in central Manchester. The original use of this building was as a walk-in dispensary for sick children, before either of the two children's hospitals at Pendlebury and Booth Hall were built, but over the years it had gradually developed into its new role as an outpatients department for Pendlebury. It was a totally inappropriate building for the work being done there, though the work itself was excellent. Our clinic was in the basement, the most unlikely place for a clinic that I have ever seen. This underground area had corridors leading away into seeming oblivion; some of them housed long metal racks with the patients' notes on them. At the far end of a long underground corridor was the room where the review clinic was held. This large room was rather haphazardly partitioned into three sections, using curtained screens fixed to tubular steel frames on castors. The screens were versatile but not very adequate and did not create any sound proofing. The waiting area for the clinic was just outside the door. On the wall was a clock; it had been wired incorrectly, so the hands on it went backwards. Children played about, noisily sometimes, but most of the consultations with the other patients and their families could be heard.

First of all, each child had to be weighed and measured. Then we proceeded to the desk on the left, beside which was a bed for the patient; here we saw Dr Evans. We progressed to the second desk where sat the joint specialist, who advised on damaged joints. Thirdly, we moved to the last desk where we met the dentist, who cared for children with bleeding problems at the Manchester Dental Hospital, but did interim reviews at this clinic. We got to know her well over the years; she was a kindly lady, always welcoming and helpful and we missed her when she retired. A physiotherapist was on hand to give advice on exercises for joints that had suffered spontaneous bleeds. Many of the boys with haemophilia had bad spontaneous bleeds into their joints, causing immense pain and damage. The nurses from the haemophilia centre at Pendlebury completed the team. We built good relationships with these nurses as time went on and of course they got to know us very well. It was comforting and reassuring to see their familiar faces on our visits. One of the nurses, Sister Alex Shaw, was especially supportive to Ros over the years.

Cryo had proved to be an effective treatment for Ros's bleeds so far, but we found out that there was a shortage of UK produced supplies. We wrote to our member of parliament (MP), Andrew Bennett, about this, expressing our concern and, as MPs do, he passed our letter to Dr David Owen, who was then junior minister for health. We were concerned that imported blood products from the USA were made up from paid donors, some of whom were certainly drug users and others whose life style could be classed as unhealthy. Our letter said, in part, *although two preparations for the treatment of this disorder, cryoprecipitate and freeze-dried factor VIII, were discovered in this country and are now widely used in other countries, supplies of cryoprecipitate are available for only two thirds of the estimated demand in this country and supplies of factor VIII are very severely limited. You will appreciate that, in addition to the humanitarian reasons for treating haemophiliacs whenever possible, lack of treatment can result in internal bleeding into the joints and consequent permanent crippling. Therefore the practical cost of caring for permanent cripples (sic) must be used to balance the admittedly high cost involved in the preparation of factor VIII. Further, it is possible that, if treatment of and research into the causes of blood clotting disorders is allowed to continue unhampered by financial restriction, more economical methods of treatment will be discovered. Therefore we hope that you will watch to ensure that the Government decision to allocate more money for the preparation of factor VIII is implemented so that adequate supplies will become available in the near future.* The reply the following month from Dr David Owen to our MP, and forwarded to us, outlined the measures that he had introduced to ensure that the supply of blood products would match demand within two years. (*The full text of this letter is given in Appendix 1*). This correspondence gave us continuing anxiety about there being enough blood products available. Lack of these could cause severe problems for the haemophiliac boys and for Ros too. Little did we know that many years on we would be constantly penning letters to our MP and to the department of health over a related serious issue.

It was Ros's second Christmas with us and we decided to spend it with the grandparents in Bath. John's brother and family were coming too so we looked forward to a few happy days together. Ros's cousin, Linda, was older than Ros and Philip was just two months. We decorated the Christmas tree, visited the Evens grandparents at nearby Keynsham and settled down to enjoy Christmas. Great was the excitement on Christmas day with two toddlers and a tiny baby. One of the things we gave Ros was a doll's bed that I had kept since my childhood. It was flimsy, made of plywood and painted pink, with little pixies for decoration on the bedhead. I had sewn some new bedding for it and was looking forward to seeing Ros use it for her dolls and teddies. Alas, Ros had not forgotten how to bounce around and five minutes before Christmas tea, in her excitement she bounced on some cushions, fell and cut her gum on the edge of this doll's bed. We knew immediately that the wound would need treatment as it was bleeding slowly but steadily. The nearest haemophilia centre was in the Bristol Children's Hospital next to the Bristol Royal Infirmary about twelve miles away. The roads were not busy and we were soon there. As it was Christmas Day there was very little activity in the hospital, but there was a doctor on call. He could not see very well into Ros's little mouth to examine the site of the bleeding but agreed to treat her with some cryo. After the injection was done we discussed with him our anxieties over recent experiences with Ros and suggested to him that even with the cryo she might bleed for some time yet. He agreed to admit her for observation. We were shown on to a small ward, quite unlike the big Borchardt ward at Pendlebury, and settled Ros in. The blood was still oozing slowly from her mouth and I sat and mopped at it every few minutes, until about midnight, while Ros dozed fitfully.

Behind one of the curtains used for screening the beds was a long table, laden with Christmas food. The nurses, who were very kind, kept urging us to help ourselves to some of this sumptuous feast, but I could eat little. I was so anxious about Ros; the Christmas feel to the day was long gone. John went back to his parents, while I slept for a few hours in a cubicle in one of the day rooms downstairs. It was very public, being glass all round, but fortunately there were very few people about. I returned to the ward early on Boxing Day morning.

28

It was just as well that Ros had been admitted. She looked pale and was weak and fretful; the blood was still oozing. The nurses kept a constant watch over her and over me, too. One particular nurse was so kind and came often to ask me, "Are you alright my darling?" in her broad Bristolian accent. When I looked near to tears, which was often, she brought a soothing cup of tea and with it her moral support. I felt very ragged emotionally sitting there beside Ros, not able to help her. She was given more cryo, but continued to get weaker as the day went on, vomiting any drinks or liquid food.

John came back to join me and together we tried to keep Ros lying on her side, so that she couldn't swallow the blood, but this meant continually mopping up. We got through sheets and sheets of hospital blue tissue roll. Every minute of this ghastly day grew longer and longer as the dark crimson blood, the stuff of life, slowly oozed from her. Ros was very distressed all day, neither being interested enough to play or settled enough to sleep. She became paler and paler. We felt so worried, tired out and distressed by the whole situation. The little world we had created around Ros's hospital bed did not allow us to think too hard about what was going on elsewhere. Outside the hospital it was still Boxing Day, a holiday for relaxing with family and friends. By 4.30pm the doctors had decided to give her a blood transfusion and once that was set up John and I drove back to Bath for some rest, leaving her in their good hands.

The next day we were back at the hospital early. Ros seemed no better, in fact she seemed much worse, still oozing blood and very fretful and restless. Her lips were now pale pink and her skin deathly white. The doctor came to set up more blood for transfusion. It seemed to be the only way that he could think of to alleviate this relentless bleeding. A paediatrician was called to evaluate the situation. He decided that it was a job for a dentist and said he would call one in (it was still the Christmas holiday). He also suggested that the only way they would get a real look at the site of Ros's bleeding would be under anaesthetic.

Ros had had an awful morning and so had we. We had been hoping and praying for this bleeding to stop. It was hard just sitting there waiting – waiting for the doctor's decision, waiting for time to pass, waiting for her to be better. Eventually Ros was taken to theatre for investigation. We were given a meal ticket and had some lunch in the hospital canteen while she was gone.

After her visit to theatre we were taken to see her in the baby care unit. She was in an oxygen tent, where she was to remain for 24 hours of intensive care. The dentist had applied a special dressing to the wound on Ros's gum and the bleeding had stopped at last. How thankful we were to see our daughter without blood oozing from her. She already looked different, much more like our pretty baby, but still very pale. Now Ros, aged 21 months, felt like talking again. Half an hour after coming out of theatre, she sat up in her oxygen tent and called, "Dinner, dinner". We were amazed! A nurse brought her some jelly, which she gobbled at speed. She began to look pink again, the pink gradually suffusing her whole face and the pale white disappearing as we watched. Soon Ros was heard asking for "Pugging, pugging", in her weary little voice. We knew then that she was on the road to recovery. The nurse brought her some ice cream and that, too, went down well.

Although she was still attached to a drip and had it splinted to her tiny arm, Ros made such good progress that by 8.00pm she was able to go back to the main ward. We settled her down for the night and crept away to Bath for some much needed sleep. We were both exhausted.

The next morning Ros was pleased to see us and did not cry. She had had her drip splint removed and could move freely, so this made her more cheerful. We had a quiet day with her as she caught up on rest, play and soft food. The dentist called in to check on her and we were able to thank him personally. Ros spent one more day at the children's hospital, trying to play about normally on her wobbly little legs. We got the all-clear to go home after Ros had been an in-patient for five days and drove back to Stockport the next day. We will never forget Ros's second Christmas.

So we came to the end of our first full year looking after Ros as a severe bleeder. It had been an eventful year indeed. We were still asking, "Why?" "Why did Ros have this disease?" "What was it all about?" "Why was there no cure?" "Why did we all have to suffer?"

We were beginning to recognise that vWd was much more serious than we had first thought. One example of this was the fact that we had been advised to contact our local ambulance station, which was close by. We told them of Ros's condition and were assured that they would come to us immediately if we needed them and take us to Pendlebury, not just to the nearest hospital.

We were relieved that the bleeds had been intermittent, so that we were not at the hospital every week. Ros was such a happy little girl. We gave thanks for all the good times that we had had and continued to enjoy her company.

I went down the road, meeting Juliet, then John & Rosamund, then Ben & Caroline. By tea time about half the party were back all very thirsty.
John & Juliet & Rosamund went off to Ambleside to get the proofs of the photographs, dropping Mary off near Dove Cottage. (Rosamund, on learning that they were going to the photographers, "I smile".)
I watched Bryony & Beth having showers – they were absolutely filthy – then sat and read 'Owl Tried to Sleep' to Caroline, with Matthew doing the chorus lines. Then read another exciting tale to Richard & Bryony. Juliet & Hilary arrived with photo proofs.

Richard and Dorothy Evens with their grandchildren
l-r Bryony, Caroline, Richard (standing), Ros, Beth, Matthew on
the occasion of their Ruby Wedding August 1976

Chapter Four

I have described in some detail what it was like to see someone you love suffering with a bleeding disorder. We had increasingly to try and describe to people what was wrong with our beautiful child. We had to explain how long it might take for her bleeding to stop. For people with normal blood it took only a few seconds, minutes at most and was a minor problem for them. They could apply a plaster or bandage, put a cold key down the back or pinch the nostrils and it was all over.

With Ros it was not all over until we had travelled twelve miles, sat in a hospital for several hours or days, watched her go from pink to white and back to pink again and then brought her home, possibly still anaemic and rather wobbly on her little legs. It all seemed incredibly awful – the journey, the waiting around, the fact that it was happening at all.

Sometimes I would tell myself that I was dreaming, I would wake up one morning and the nightmare would be over. She would be a healthy baby again and we would live happily ever after. There was nothing, apparently, wrong with her. It was all unseen, hidden away and nobody could tell what might be amiss. The bruises, I suppose, were a clue, but people were more likely to think that Ros was being knocked about, than to think of any rare disease.

Life, however, went on routinely. The adoption agency encouraged us to put together the story of Ros's adoption to share with her. Commonly called 'Telling' by adopters and social workers, the format suggested was a simple scrapbook, with a written storyline that a young child could comprehend. Sharing this story early in the child's life, before he or she could properly understand, meant that the word 'adoption' was always known to the child. I completed a scrapbook for Ros which was most helpful in explaining adoption to her. It enabled us talk to about her 'funny blood' as well, in order that she should understand that her blood was different from the norm and that she would grow up with that idea, as with adoption. We must have done well with this 'storytelling' as, much to my surprise one day when we were in our local library, Ros, aged three and a half, trotted up to the librarian behind the desk and announced in a loud voice, "You know, I've got funny blood!" The librarian looked suitably shocked!

Before Ros arrived I had been running a playgroup for pre-school children in the local church hall. A Quaker friend, Erica, suggested that I should visit a local nursery centre called Charnwood. Charnwood had been started by Grace Wyatt in her own home in Heaton Moor, Stockport, in the early 1960's. Grace was a trained nursery teacher and while at home with her pre-school children she invited her neighbour's handicapped child to play with them, as there was no provision for her elsewhere. Soon other parents brought their disabled children and the numbers grew. It was not long before Grace started a small morning nursery school. In the afternoons Grace invited parents to bring their handicapped and disabled young children and babies to play and to be stimulated, offering at the same time a chance for parents who felt isolated to get together.

I went with my playgroup colleagues to visit this nursery. It was now housed in a rather cramped old coach house behind a dentist's consulting rooms in the centre of Heaton Moor. Grace's neighbours had complained to the council about her home run nursery and they had closed it down. The father of one of the nursery children saw that Grace very much wanted to continue her work and he offered her the coach house which was in the grounds of his dental practice. I was impressed by all I saw on this first visit and through Erica kept in touch with what went on there. Demand for places was great and Grace rarely turned children away. After eight years the lease of the coach house ran out. Charnwood was by now a registered charity and was soon able to move into a rented property, a large Victorian house in nearby Mauldeth Road.

My experience of working with children and of the recent running of the playgroup led me to think that Ros could benefit from the high quality play materials that Charnwood provided, and she would be further stimulated by meeting and playing alongside other young children. Ros and I made our first visit, to see if Grace would allow us to come to the afternoon group.

Grace was a charming lady, good-looking and elegant. She had a deep Christian concern for all the children in her care and much compassion for the parents, particularly for those of children with disabilities. She could see what a bright little girl Ros was, but she had some concern over her bleeding problem. She told me that she had always said she would accept any child at Charnwood, except those with haemophilia or brittle bones. These two conditions, Grace felt, carried great risks to their sufferers in the general rough and tumble of a nursery school or play session, where even with the best supervision accidents could occur. I described some of the bleeding episodes that Ros had suffered and explained the necessary treatment. After some discussion, Grace agreed that it would be all right for Ros to come to the afternoon opportunity groups, provided that I was fully responsible for her. And so my long connection with Charnwood began.

We went along for our first hour at the nursery. It was a most successful session. Ros enjoyed all the new and stimulating activities and I was glad to meet other parents and staff and have time to talk about Ros and her strange condition. No one there had ever heard of vWd, so I explained her hidden complaint to anyone who asked. We continued to go on Fridays. Ros really enjoyed her sessions and was happy afterwards. After a few months Grace, who had been watching her progress, decided that one of her volunteers, a nurse, could take Ros off my hands just for a short while, giving me a much needed break. This was a big step forward for both of us. Ros was a sociable little girl and did not mind being taken off to play without me. She was eager to learn new skills and make new friends, though when you are only two years old this could be problematic. But no one bashed her on the head with a brick or pushed her into the sandpit. The worst thing that happened to Ros in all the years that she played there was one day in the garden when she fell into some rose bushes, acquiring some evil looking scratches! As Grace and her staff and volunteers got to know Ros they relaxed and eventually agreed that she could join the morning nursery school. To start with I was to be her support person.

I was so glad to have found Charnwood. I liked all the staff and volunteers; they were kind and compassionate and gave of themselves wholeheartedly in their care of the children. There was a calm and nurturing atmosphere which helped me enormously as I talked about Ros's problems and my hopes and fears for the future. Although no one knew of any other children with the same condition, there were several other parents of children with similarly isolating rare diseases, so I did not feel so alone.

When Ros was still tiny and as she had cut several baby teeth we were advised to take her to the dental hospital. We had met the dentist at the review clinic and had an appointment to see her. I thought Ros was extremely small to be going to the dentist. However off we went into Manchester, to the children's section of this large university teaching hospital for our first appointment. As the dental nurse ushered us into the treatment area I said, "Do you take them this small?" She laughed and assured me they did. There was a comfortable no-nonsense atmosphere in this unit, no screaming children, just calm busyness. Ros was allowed to ride up and down on the dentist's chair and explore all the things she wanted to explore, so this first visit was very relaxed. The dentist advised starting dental care early, which would be to Ros's advantage for developing good habits in teeth and mouth care.

When Ros was two years old John and I decided to apply to adopt again. We hoped for another baby, though there were fewer babies available for adoption. The staff at the haemophilia centre had advised us that bringing Ros up in a family with siblings would be better for her than being the only child, wrapped in cotton wool and over protected. We had agreed that this sort of sheltered life was not to be for Ros though, naturally, we would still need to take lots of precautions for her safety. We wrote to the NCH and received a favourable reply. Our application was being followed up and soon a social worker came to make her assessments of us as a family. Having been already approved, the NCH were keen now to see how we were getting on with Ros. The necessary paper work was done quite quickly and our application was submitted. Within a week of our application we had been approved again and were once more on a waiting list.

Ros was becoming quite assertive in her own little way. While in hospital for three days she became absorbed in the ward's play activities. When the time came for going home I said, "Let's go home now". She replied, "No!" I had a fear of her becoming too attached to hospital life; I did not want to spend a moment longer at the hospital than was necessary. While we were spending a few days with my brother Nick, his wife Hilary and their two boys, Ros insisted on climbing to the top of the climbing frame in their garden saying, "Don't hold me". Naturally enough she was pushing for her independence, but I often had to hold my breath while she performed some fairly normal activity. We had to learn to let go, physically as well as emotionally. I resolved to try not to nag Ros too much and before breakfast one day left her to her own devices. She promptly had a fall in the bathroom and developed a nasty bruise. I wondered whether it was worth it!

I had a chat with Grace about leaving Ros on her own at the morning session at Charnwood during the next autumn term. She was now two and a half years old, very bright and eager to learn. Grace still wanted me to be her support person. Small bleeds were occurring on and off and I managed to cope with these, applying frozen packs if it seemed advisable or giving Ros an ice lolly to suck. Reading stories or playing quiet games helped to reduce her blood pressure and slowed any bleeding. From June of one year until July of the following year we managed to cope without any treatment at hospital. It was the longest stretch we ever had without visits to Pendlebury and to this day we do not know why she was so comparatively bleed free for that time.

On Christmas Eve we had a letter from the NCH. The outlook was not so bright for adopting a baby as single mothers were being encouraged to keep their babies. There was still a chance we would get a baby, but our wait was going to be much longer than we had anticipated. We spent Christmas quietly at home, thinking a lot about what had befallen Ros the previous Christmas.

Grace Wyatt relented and allowed Ros one session a week in the morning nursery without me. It was another milestone passed for all of us, letting others take temporary responsibility for her care.

Both John and I kept up with our interests when we could. I belonged to a local choral society and managed to get to most of the weekly rehearsals. Sometimes I had a Quaker committee or meeting to go to. John had his interest in buses as a hobby and occasionally entertained fellow bus enthusiasts. Now and again he took his college students on field trips. Emma, our teenage friend, came to babysit, but only when Ros was asleep, when we had a rare evening out. We were always 'on call' when away from home.

My good friend, Christine, who I had met through the Heatons' Christian Council, was often with us, bringing her two children to play with Ros. Helen was a few months older than Ros and David was still a baby. It was good to have someone to talk to while the children played. Many are the times that Christine has been on hand to help me out over the years, and I am so thankful for her friendship. We travelled now and then to visit the grandparents or to see other family members and cousins.

Life was so normal when Ros was bleed free that we sometimes forgot about vWd. Then it would suddenly manifest itself again and our anxiety for Ros would reappear. To her credit, Ros was very resilient about her condition, all the driving to and from Pendlebury, the long waiting times and then the treatment. I cannot recall her ever complaining about having needles stuck into her. After the first few times she just accepted that it was part of her life. I would sit beside her, trying to be reassuring while hating to see the needles going in, but she did not need me to distract her, as she watched what was happening with interest.

These intravenous injections were slow in preparation, the cryo taking time to thaw out before being drawn up into a syringe. Once the syringe was ready the doctor or nurse would select a vein for inserting the needle, usually in the inside of the elbow, sometimes in the back of the hand. Very often when Ros was tiny it was hard to find a vein. The staff were always outstandingly calm and cheerful, even if they were in a hurry. The injection of the cryo was best given really slowly, so as to allow her body time to cope with it. Once during an injection, Ros's skin, face and neck went very red, her face swelled up alarmingly and she could not breathe. The doctor quickly administered a shot of antihistamine and reassured us that this was a rare allergic reaction to something in the cryo. Ros recovered immediately. This has never reoccurred.

Did Ros begin to recognise the moral support I was trying to give her, even at that tender age? Children are so reliant on good nurturing care by their parents, particularly when under five years old. I was very heartened to have her snuggle up on my lap one bedtime and hear her say, "This is a cosy place to live". The next night she followed this with, "Oh Mummy, you're such a dearie!" When children make these statements we are often amused by them. How often do we recognise that they could indicate emotional and spiritual development? Was Ros developing an emotional maturity beyond her years, coping with the knocks and traumas that her life had already brought her?

Some friends of ours owned a cottage on the east coast of Scotland, and they offered it to us for a week. We jumped at the chance of a holiday by the sea. The cottage was in the tiny hamlet of Cove, north of Berwick on Tweed and stood near to the edge of a high cliff top looking out to sea. A short walk down a rough path brought us to the tiny harbour and beach. It was a marvellous holiday spot and we returned a few more times. We had taken a covering letter from Dr Evans with us in case we needed to go to the Edinburgh treatment centre, but on this first visit did not use it. Ros did have a fall on some

Juliet and Ros on Arthur's Seat, Edinburgh, July 1976

rough tarmac one day and grazed both knees badly. The only way to control the bleeding was to wrap more and more bandages around her knees, leaving any dirt to extricate itself through the gooey layer of antiseptic cream I had first applied.

Due to Ros's frequent and persistent nosebleeds we were introduced to a new phenomenon in treatment – the nose pack. Ros's nose started to bleed very early one morning and despite trying to stop it we had no luck, so set off for Pendlebury around 5.30am. She was given the usual cryo but spent the rest of the day oozing blood on and off. We went back to the hospital at 4.00pm, where more cryo was administered and her nose was packed with adrenalin soaked gauze. This looked awful and was very uncomfortable. We had to stop her fiddling with it all the time. Taking it out gently was a delicate manoeuvre, as I did not want to set off a further bleed. We were lucky on this first occasion. There were many more occasions when Ros had to suffer this rather undignified procedure.

Ros was now attending Charnwood for two mornings a week and having a really good time. It was a real joy to me to see her getting on so well and avoiding accidents. I had discussed schooling with Grace, as I knew that we would need to get Ros's name down in good time. Grace suggested that we should visit a school near Charnwood, which was further from our house but had a very good reputation. We made an appointment to meet the headmaster and duly went along and were given a very warm welcome. The head welcomed Ros too and allowed her to wander around his office while John and I talked. We were shown briefly round the school and liked the atmosphere there. The head warned us that we were not in his catchment area and said that if we did decide to send Ros there he could foresee that some difficulties might arise with after school friendships and parties. We would have to travel to help Ros keep up with her school friends.

Our local school was only five minutes walk away from home, but we had heard that the headmaster there was unfriendly and not very approachable. However, due to its close proximity we thought we should go and take a look. We made an appointment to see the headmaster after which we would decide where we would like Ros to go. We entered the head's smoke ridden office at this second school and Ros began to wander about, just as she had done in the previous school. The headmaster did not like this and to this day I can remember his caustic remark. He said, "Children are not allowed on this side of the desk". Strict though he seemed to be, he agreed to take Ros at the start of the new school year in September 1978 but under certain conditions. I had to be on call at home all the time Ros was in school and he would not allow her to stay for school dinner. We decided to take this place.

The time came for our visit to the annual review clinic at Gartside Street. The joint specialist there had previously reserved judgement on whether Ros would have trouble with joint or muscle bleeds. Now he advised us that, in his opinion, Ros was very unlikely to have any trouble of this sort and he dismissed us from his section of the clinic with a wave of the hand saying, "Forget it". I remember thinking I would reserve judgement on this. We discovered much later that this specialist was a rheumatologist and not an orthopaedic surgeon.

How the fates conspire! Little did the man know about Ros. It was only twelve days later that she had a sore foot. We were at a guest-house in Grasmere and had walked round the village in the morning. Ros had a bad cough and had not slept too well, so I put her to bed for a sleep in the afternoon. When she got up her foot was sore and tender and she would not move it or walk on it. I had been advised by the haemophilia staff that a crepe bandage strapping would support a limb if a bleed was suspected. We strapped up Ros's foot and ankle. Next day she walked normally over some rough ground, but by the evening the ankle was causing trouble again. On the Monday morning, at home again, it was more swollen than previously, so we went to Pendlebury. A small bleed in the ankle was diagnosed and cryo was given. We were told to keep Ros resting; she must not walk at all for a while. She was very good about all this and luckily was still small enough to be carried about easily. Going to Pendlebury meant that Ros had missed her morning session at Charnwood. We told them what had happened and they arranged to lend us a blue McClaren buggy to wheel her about in. After a couple of days the ankle was much better.

Excerpt from Ros's blog, 17 July 2008, about a particularly persistent shoulder bleed

Blood drains from under me plaster

tissues blot it

don't bleed on floor

attempt to mix bottles of treatment

don't drip on table

mop it with tissue

fill my syringe

get blood on my hands

all over my arm

hope window cleaner isn't due

put on tourniquet

put tourniquet on other arm cos need to mop up bleeding arm

hold tissue on shoulder with chin

stick needle in

inject stuff

stop half way through

wipe blood up

start again

finish

take needle out

don't care if blood spills on table

or floor

wait

dab

still going

wait

dab

wait

dab

still going

take off blood soaked plasters

still going

put on clean plasters

clean arm with steret wipe

another steret wipe

another

wonder why didn't just have another shower

watch plaster

watch plaster

nothing.

No blood.

Hooorah.

Gum still going tho.

Chapter Five

Friends and acquaintances stopped me in the street. "How's Ros?" they would ask. They asked it both when they knew that Ros had been having trouble and when she was bleed free. "Fine", I would answer. If Ros was going through a good patch I would say, nonchalantly, "She's had no bleeds for ages". It was like tempting fate; every time this happened Ros would have a bleed the next day! It was uncanny. I wondered about issuing bulletins on her health, royal family style, just to keep people informed. I began to notice that people did not ask me how *I* was. I felt quite envious of families who just seemed to tick along, day after day, without crises, while we were running about after Ros and getting quite exhausted. However, we refused to bend before this frightening disease and continued as a family to make plans for days out, holidays and future events, always ensuring that we would have reasonable access to medical help, preferably a haemophilia treatment centre.

We had now been on the adoption waiting list for nearly two years. The NCH contacted us to say that they were regionalising all their work and that we would soon get visits from a social worker based in their Warrington office. Did this mean some progress towards adopting a brother or sister for Ros? However, when we had our first visit from a social worker, the news was not so good. As there were so few babies waiting for placement it would be some time yet, if ever, that a baby would be placed with us. The social worker asked us to consider the possibility of fostering a toddler or older child, with a view to adoption. There were many children languishing in care homes who needed loving families, as I knew from my previous work in children's homes. I still wanted another baby, but I could understand the difficulties. We both wanted Ros to have a brother or sister and realised that having an older child might be an option.

Our nearby primary school contacted us about Ros starting there in September. We had decided that it would be the right school for her because of its close proximity, but when we went for an initial visit I was surprised to find that the staff had not been told about her bleeding condition. We had discussed it with the headmaster at our first meeting. Fortunately, I was able to give Ros's teacher some details and it was agreed with her, as it had been with the head, that I must be 'on call' while Ros was in school. That first term Ros went to either morning or afternoon sessions until the half-term break. She then did a full day, coming home for lunch as the head had not relented over his original conditions. This seemed fair enough. I could check that all was well with Ros, but it was tiring for both of us, making the short walk every couple of hours.

Charnwood had helped me to feel positive about leaving Ros with strangers to look after her, and she settled into school very quickly and happily. She was a sociable little girl and made new friends easily. She especially liked a little girl called Kitty, who was in the same class. They soon became firm friends. Kitty and her parents had been exiled from Chile under the Pinochet regime. Kitty's father, Daniel, had taken a job at the University of Manchester Institute of Science and Technology (UMIST). My abiding memory is of seeing Kitty, aged five, so petite and beautiful, being wheeled to school on the handlebars of Daniel's bike. We got to know the family when Kitty, her mother Veronica and baby sister Karen, came to play and chat after school.

In earlier discussions with our social worker we had been offered the chance of attending six weekly foster parent training sessions. After considering whether we could both go, we agreed to join them. Friends rallied round to babysit Ros for us. We felt the sessions would be valuable experience when it came to our fostering or adopting a brother or sister for Ros. We began the assessment process for long-term fostering with a view to adoption. At the same time a new social worker, Sue, began paying us regular visits. In a way it seemed rather unnecessary, since we were already approved adopters, but if that was the way to go, who were we to argue.

During the summer of this year there occurred two 'firsts' for Ros and for us. We bought her her first bike and she had her first loose baby tooth. Ros pedalled enthusiastically up and down our drive, while we held our breath. Stabilisers do have their uses and those little back wheels helped to prevent any major accidents as Ros learnt to ride. The loose tooth, however, was much more problematic and the gum bled heavily. The dentist wanted to be involved each time a tooth came loose, so we embarked on the first of many round trips to the dental hospital in central Manchester and on to Pendlebury for cryo. It did not take me long to realise that it was quicker to go to Pendlebury first for the treatment and then to the dentist for advice on the way back. Whichever way we went, it made a huge hole in our day.

This summer I, too, had a first. This was the infant school outing and Ros was not allowed to go unless I went too. It was a boiling hot day in July and the trip was to a local safari park. In two coaches ninety-six infants and staff drove through the safari park with all the windows and roof lights shut tight!

I met the mother of a little boy with haemophilia, who also lived in Stockport. I introduced them both to Charnwood. Grace now had had experience of coping with Ros and agreed to take this little boy into the morning nursery and asked me to be his helper. I was happy to do this, and to become involved again with the work at Charnwood.

My knowledge and understanding of haemophilia and of vWd was gradually increasing. Helping to care for this little boy and talking with his mother made me realise how much I now knew. I began to feel that I was a bit of an expert on bleeding disorders, though if you had asked me to explain the genetics of either condition, or talk about chromosomes, I would have struggled! But I was sure that I knew more than the general public, who still thought that haemophiliacs were males who bled to death if they cut themselves. I knew different; I knew that there were effective treatments for haemophiliacs and that their quality of life was improving.

For Ros, even with vWd, life was good. Her bleeds were mostly slow oozes that became debilitating if they were prolonged. She was not getting spontaneous joint bleeds like the boys, but we knew her joints and muscles could be affected after falls or accidents.

Our fostering application report was finalised by the social worker and was due to go before the NCH committee for approval. Sue came on her final visit, bringing with her a more senior social worker. We felt we were very near to being approved. A few weeks went by and then Sue phoned. Was it good news about our fostering application? No, it was something quite different. Sue asked if we would be interested in a possible adoption. She told us there was a three year old boy living in the Isle of Man who was waiting to join a new family and asked us if we would like to know more about him. What a thrill! John and I talked it over and rang back, asking her for more details. We arranged a day when she could come and share them with us.

After this meeting we agreed that we liked the sound of this three year old – no baby things needed, no nappies, no sleepless nights, but a ready made little boy who could play with Ros and be company for her. We felt ready to accept this new challenge and Ros seemed keen on the idea. Sue warned that there could be a few problems as Paul, as he was called, had moved around and had already had a number of carers in his young life. This moved me at the time and I was full of heartache for this little boy. He needed some stability and a chance to settle down with a new family. One of the reasons for springing this possible adoption on us after all the foster parent training was that the agency wanted to place Paul in his permanent home before he started school. At the time I thought this was reasonable enough. With hindsight I realised that Paul's placement was done in a hurry and this caused problems later on.

We decided to go ahead. Sue arranged a day visit to the Isle of Man for a Saturday in October for us to meet Paul. We met her at Manchester Airport and after a short flight we were circling in over the runway at Ronaldsway. The island looked particularly good on this bright autumn morning. A taxi took us to Ramsey, in the north, and to the only children's home on the island, Dalmeny, run by the NCH. A cheerful, brown haired lady, Sister Beryl, welcomed us warmly. She had worked in the children's home for a number of years and cared deeply for all the children who lived there. As soon as she saw Ros she said that she knew her. "How like her mother she is!" was her unexpected comment. Ros had been in her care for a short time before her move to Frodsham. We knew that Ros had been born on the island, but knew little about her moves before coming to us. During the day, Sister Beryl hunted for and found a photograph of a baby in a pram, which she said was Ros. It was quite hard to tell. She called Ros her 'little Mary Mouse'. Sister Beryl knew many families on the island through her work with their children and she was to prove a helpful contact later when we needed information.

After some refreshment and an initial chat Sister Beryl went to fetch Paul. We heard running footsteps along the corridor outside, the door burst open and there he was! He was quite small for his age, rather stocky, with a head of thick fair hair, blue eyes and colouring much the same as Ros. I felt pleased – he was cute and very appealing. The strangeness of the situation was swept aside as we were shown round the large, rambling building and talked to the other staff and children.

Juliet, Paul and Ros
near Dalmeny Children's Home

Playing and spending time with Paul was the best way to find out more about him. After lunch with everyone together, we were allowed a couple of hours alone with Paul. Dalmeny was situated high up on a cliff, overlooking the sea and the obvious place to go to was the nearby seashore. This we did; the children ran along happily together and played about on the beach. Observing their acceptance of each other as they played was encouraging. Our decision was still fraught with unknowns. All too soon our time was up; the flight home was at teatime. Our visit, though short, had been very exciting and positive.

A further visit to Dalmeny was arranged for the following weekend and we were booked to stay for two nights. The NCH made all the arrangements – we just had to adjust to our new role as prospective parents for a second time.

Next weekend we flew once again from Manchester Airport. We arrived at Dalmeny just before lunch. Paul was pleased to see us again and we were thrilled to see him and know that he had not forgotten us. We now had two days to try and get to know this little boy, who would soon become a member of our family. Time alone with him was a bonus, but we were constrained from going far because of meals at Dalmeny. Initially the weather was fine, so we were on the beach or in the nearby park and we did some shopping in Ramsey. The second day was dull and damp and kept us indoors. Our bed and breakfast accommodation was a farmhouse some miles out of Ramsey. A local swimming gala was being held and all the nearby hotels and B and B's were taken up with visitors to this. We had to rely on a member of staff being free to drive us out to our farmhouse, and that meant fitting in with the Dalmeny timetable. Thus it was that, despite our wish to be there for Paul's bedtime and morning routine, we were unable to be there at those important times. In our somewhat euphoric state of becoming parents again it never occurred to us to be pushy and insist on staying into the evening to see Paul into bed, then have a taxi back to the farmhouse! Ros was tired after the day's adventures. Mercifully, she had no bleeding problems, falls or accidents during the weekend.

Very quickly it was time for our return home. We felt sad at leaving Paul in the children's home, but were now firmly convinced that we would like to bring him home with us as soon as possible. We agreed this with the NCH and waited for them to make the arrangements.

They suggested November 5th, only a week away. There was a lot to be done to get ready for Paul's arrival. We were having a downstairs toilet installed, as carrying Ros up and down stairs when immobilised by a bleed was becoming more of a problem. There was cleaning to be done after the building work and there was the back bedroom to be prepared for Paul.

We had ordered a large buggy, the McClaren Major, designed to carry children up to eight stone in weight, and similar to the one we had borrowed from Charnwood. I had carried Ros to school a few times, when hospital staff advised rest for aches and pains in her feet and legs. She was getting too heavy for me to continue doing this. I did not want Ros to miss any more schooling than was necessary, given the time already taken up with hospital appointments and visits. The headmaster had summoned me one day when I had carried Ros into school, to say that he did not think she should be in school if she was immobile. The teachers, however, were happy for Ros to sit in the classroom at playtimes and a school nurse was on hand to help out. So the buggy would be most useful in helping me to take Ros to school and it was delivered during these few hectic days.

The week went by very fast. A member of staff would travel with Paul, stay overnight and then return. The adoption process was to start as soon as he arrived. There was to be no initial fostering. This was a pity, as fostering might have given us a financial allowance. Adoption allowances were introduced when our children had reached adulthood. We could have done with some extra cash while both children were growing up.

All too quickly the great day came. I was very excited at the prospect of having another child. It would help to bring a balance into our care of Ros, by not smothering her with fuss and attention when she had bleeds. Our aim was to let her lead as normal and active a life as possible.

At the airport I nervously awaited the arrival of my new son. I had no idea what the future would hold, but I expected some challenges ahead in bringing into our family a child who had had a very unstable first few years.

Paul came through the arrivals hall at Manchester Airport, with the member of staff. His few possessions, a teddy bear and some clothes, were contained in a black plastic bag. He spotted me immediately, rushed up to me and asked, "Where's Daddy?" I told him Daddy was at work. John and I had agreed that one new parent meeting Paul might be easier for him, also giving him the idea that Daddy would not always be around as he had a full time job. Paul then proceeded to lead his careworker and me a merry dance, running off in all directions towards stairs, escalators and other dangers. He had to be firmly but kindly restrained before he met with an accident.

We walked safely back to the car park and drove home to a house that Paul had never seen before. That was hard to take, for him and for me. He coped by rushing about everywhere, opening every door, cupboard and drawer until he was satisfied that he had seen everything. He was very excited.

The first few days of our new family life were chaotic and exhausting. Paul was a very energetic little boy and quite demanding at times, but he played about happily and slept well. It was very different from having only Ros, a quiet child, who could play by herself. Adjusting to another child was hard work. I needed to keep an eye on Ros, in case she was jealous of Paul, but she enjoyed his company and liked to have someone to play with. The first week it rained solidly, good November weather, and I had my work cut out just getting both children ready three times a day to take Ros to school. Ten days after his arrival it was Paul's fourth birthday. We invited Christine's two children, Helen and David, and Leon, the son of another friend, who was the same age as Paul, to have birthday tea. Family and friends sent cards and presents to a little boy they had not yet met, but it was then that I realised how different this adoption was to having a new baby and being showered with cards, gifts and good wishes. I felt disappointed that Paul had less fuss, but of course he didn't notice. He was thrilled with his new battery operated train and track and played with them constantly.

Sue visited us weekly for a few weeks, which was helpful as I had many questions for her. Her visits began to drop off, and she only came every few months. Over the next few years we often felt the need for her support and for support from the adoption agency, but this proved to be very patchy and eventually became non-existent. Paul's placement, from the residential care home to our new family, had occurred within the short space of sixteen days. This began to worry me. The explanations given at the time – the need for permanent placement before school and the expenses that would have been incurred by us making too many visits to the Isle of Man – had been plausible enough. What I was to learn later about the placing of children with new families was to reinforce those early feelings that this had not been a satisfactory way to carry out a placement.

I started taking Paul to the afternoon groups at Charnwood.

Everyone was most welcoming but I had to keep close to him as he was extremely active and his behaviour very unpredictable in a group of children. Lacking concentration, he could not settle to anything for very long. Grace Wyatt, on first seeing him, looked at his sweet little face and said, "Beautiful". I felt proud to be his new mum.

Ros – some early school work

Chapter Six

Though it was wonderful to have another child, meeting the demands of this lively four year old was very different to adopting a baby. We were accustomed to the stresses of coping with Ros's condition. Now we had to face additional everyday challenges.

Paul needed much love and reassurance and frequently displayed difficult behaviours during his settling in. He was robustly active and physically demanding, but at the same time so beautiful and lovable. He cried out to be cared for, yet was very defensive. All that role play and discussion at the foster parent meetings seemed inapplicable when confronted by this small, angry person. He got on well with Ros, for which I was enormously grateful. She accepted him as a brother and a companion to play with. He was for a time very reliant on her and followed her about; she tolerated this in her calm, pleasant way. He seemed to understand that he must be careful with her and we tried hard not to exclude him from decisions about her treatment, for example, whether we should go to the hospital before or after tea. We tried hard, too, to keep a balance of both children receiving the same amount of attention. But what lay ahead would sap me of most of my energies, physical, mental and emotional, over the next few years.

We began to receive the quarterly bulletins from the Haemophilia Society. There were never any articles about vWd, but we gained some encouragement from the ones about haemophilia, although they always featured boys or men. We had bought a copy of the new book *Living With Haemophilia* by Dr Peter Jones, the haemophilia centre director at Newcastle. The chapters on education and employment, activities and precautions, treatments and bleeding episodes were useful. The book was geared towards boys, but just occasionally 'child' and 'children' were mentioned. There were a small number of references to vWd and I found myself returning to these same few pages, in the hope that perhaps I would find some new insight into Ros's condition. The book became very well thumbed. We were pleased to see the first article on vWd appear in the Haemophilia Society bulletin in 1981.

The north west group of the Haemophilia Society was very active in fund-raising and other social activities. It was difficult for us to get to many of these events, as John had evening lectures to give, or we could not arrange babysitters. We did go to the annual family weekends and enjoyed them very much. For a number of years these were held in a large hotel in Blackpool or Lytham. They were always well attended and had excellent speakers and workshops. Many of the speakers were doctors active in the haemophilia centres and they kept us updated on treatments and developments in haemophilia care. The workshops were led by nurses, physiotherapists and other professionals involved in caring for haemophiliacs. It was good to share knowledge and experiences in small groups. The social aspect of the weekend was excellent, too, as over meals and in free time we got to know other families coping with a bleeding disorder. Much of the funding for these weekends came from the drug companies who produced factor VIII, so we found ourselves enjoying the luxury of hotel life for only a few pounds per head.

Dr Evans and his wife, who was also a doctor, opened their house for a Christmas party for anyone with a connection to haemophilia – parents, spouses, children and sufferers. A separate Christmas party for the children was held at Pendlebury. Dr Evans enjoyed seeing his young patients playing normally and healthily and it was good for staff and families to meet informally away from the stresses of the treatment room. He nurtured good friendships over the years with the children he cared for and their families and this has been a source of great pleasure to him.

Despite all these social events I still felt quite isolated caring for Ros. Our daily life was sometimes stress-free and at other times hectic and worrying. Was this how it was to be? I spent so many hours living with the demands of vWd that I never had time to deal with the mental anguish that it engendered. It was not so much the worry of the actual disease, it was the strain of getting through each day, coping with the extra washing and remaining alert that was challenging. Blood, hospitals, doctors, treatments, sleepless nights, exhaustion were now facets of our lives; the bleeding situations not regular but often enough to be disruptive. Even with all the contacts I had made within the haemophilia community, I still relied heavily on the help and advice that the hospital staff could give. Coping from day to day and week to week, both John and I gradually began to understand the best ways of dealing with all the bleeds.

There was absolutely no way of avoiding this relentless disease. If I sat Ros down quietly with a book to avoid any possible accident she would get a paper cut from the pages of the book. I was very aware of her bruises, dark, ugly looking things on her delicate little arms and legs. People stared at her when we were out. I was embarrassed but Ros seemed not to mind. The summer time was the worst, when in the warm weather her limbs were exposed while she was out playing, joining in the rough and tumble. On one occasion she got some deep bruising on her back after trying to give Paul 'piggy backs'.

The days were full and busy but there were many nights, too, when I was up with Ros, with nose bleeds or bleeding gums caused by her loose teeth. I had learnt early on that she would be better propped up in bed so that she could not swallow a lot of blood. On the nights when she bled, I piled up her pillows and surrounded her with old sheets and towels but, even so, in the morning her room could look like a battlefield. The drop in blood pressure during sleep sometimes helped the bleeds to come under control but the signs would still be there, stains on the bedding, screwed up bloody tissues on the floor and even bloodstains on the wall. Ros's long fair hair became matted and her mouth stuck shut with dried blood. Sometimes all this was after treatment, too, but Ros was always pleased if the tooth fairy made it through all the mess and muddle.

When Ros outgrew the buggy we obtained a smart new wheelchair for her. This folded easily and fitted in the boot of the car. She continued to have injections of cryo, though the new factor VIII freeze-dried concentrate was available for the boys with haemophilia. We applied neat adrenalin to mouth and gum bleeds and Epsikapron and Cyclokapron solutions were taken by mouth. I thought these last two were wonder drugs as they stopped the clots from breaking down too quickly. We valued the strong relationships we were developing with the haemophilia centre staff. Evening or weekend visits for treatment were usually straightforward, as the on call staff knew about Ros and could treat her accordingly. It says a lot about their caring attitude generally that, on one visit, we were handed a lost teddy bear, which had been found and kept safely for Ros.

Paul's adoption hearing came to court in the spring following his placement with us. After a long wait the judge, in a brief hearing, said nothing at all to Paul but granted the adoption order. Now we really were a family! We were so thrilled to have our own real son, who despite all his problems was a lovely little boy, with a caring nature and a happy disposition. To make the event more of a celebration we all went out for lunch with Sue, our social worker, and later in the day drove down to Somerset to see all the grandparents.

We decided to risk going to Germany, to stay with some close friends. There were some problems to sort out before Ros could travel, most importantly, good insurance cover. Dr Evans had to submit a letter saying that Ros was fit to travel. We had to find out which hospitals in Germany we could attend if she needed treatment. Luckily the two sets of families we stayed with lived close to major cities, both of which had haemophilia centres. Dr Evans told us he knew one of the doctors, and we were duly impressed and reassured when he told us that this doctor had a phone in his car. This was in 1980, before the advent of the mobile phone.

Only two things happened to cause alarm while we were away. Ros leaned over a fence to stroke a donkey, and in response it butted her quite viciously on the shoulder. She was more frightened by this than physically hurt, but I think a bruise appeared in due course. Then a loose baby tooth came out and caused a gum bleed. We phoned the haemophilia doctor for advice, using our German friend as interpreter. Thankfully, the doctor spoke good English and advised us to keep applying adrenalin and pressure to the gum. He was, he said, reluctant to give her Hemofil, the factor VIII product available, because of the possibility of antibodies. We followed his advice and luckily the bleeding eventually stopped. This baby tooth was the only one that did not require hospital attention.

Paul started school that autumn and soon both children were allowed to stay for school dinners. This was a relief to me as now each day was slightly less hectic. Both children started after school activities. Ros went to ballet. At the time I thought ballet lessons might help Ros to keep her joints exercised, but they may in fact have been instrumental in setting up small bleeds. Although she was keen to go and had friends there, ballet classes were often missed. However, she participated in two shows put on by the class and was awarded a primary ballet certificate. She and Kitty joined the local Brownie Guides that met at their school. Paul went to gymnastics. I hoped gymnastics would channel some of his excess energy and he did prove to be an excellent little gymnast, gaining many certificates.

We had put Ros in for the entrance exam to Stockport Grammar School junior section but they did not offer her a place. Ros was very disappointed as were we, too, but we were hopeful that she would get in to Cheadle Hulme School, whose junior school took children a year later, aged eight. She sat this exam and was offered a place to start in September 1982. We were pleased as we had heard good reports about this large independent school and were impressed on our first visit.

We had some concerns over Paul's health as no notes were sent from the Isle of Man concerning childhood ailments and vaccinations. We had to rely on our memory of what we had been told during our first visit to Paul, assuming that details would follow. When these medical notes failed to appear we chased up and continually nagged the various authorities until we got them, three years after his placement. Yet more hospital visits started, this time with Paul, who was seen by an Ear, Nose and Throat (ENT) specialist at Stockport Infirmary. He was put on the waiting list to have his adenoids removed. One day at school he slipped off a bench and cracked a bone in his ankle. A plaster cast was applied for a few weeks. When he went in to have his adenoids out the doctors removed the plaster at the same time. I developed a bad back from carrying him around with his plaster cast on, in addition to pushing Ros in the wheelchair up the steep slope to school.

During these busy and somewhat chaotic years our family and friends were very supportive of us. Sadly, my mother, who had been a huge help, died in the spring of 1982, which was a great loss to me. She had been a loving and helpful grandma and was so interested in our adoption process. She loved seeing the children when she could.

She had been ill with cancer for some time and I had made several visits to her and was very concerned at her condition. It has always been a source of regret that I did not spend more time with her when she was so ill. My father coped well and looked after her at home until just before she died. I wish I could have been there to help him out.

Raymond and Phyllis Batten on their
Golden Wedding Day, 1982

On a happier note the Batten grandparents celebrated their golden wedding that summer, and we joined them on their anniversary in Bath, while on holiday in Somerset. It was during this holiday that we experienced the difference between haemophilia centres, when we attended the hospital in Taunton. We were so used now to going to Pendlebury, receiving Ros's injection and any other treatment – sling, nose pack, strapping of a joint – and then going home, that we had perhaps naively, thought the same smooth system would apply elsewhere. Of course we always had a waiting time, but because we were on 'home territory' it did not seem too bad. The visit to Taunton hospital was very tedious and we felt quite frustrated by the slowness of the staff to carry out the treatment.

Ros had some swelling around her elbow, which had developed during the day and it was stiff and painful. We went as a family and reported in at the casualty department of this hospital. We had been advised to mention the name of the doctor who was in charge of haematology. We handed in our covering letter and sat back to wait. The duty doctor, sensibly I suppose, arranged for Ros to have an X-ray. This proved clear but the doctor then decided that we must attend the children's unit, which was in another part of the town. We had difficulty finding this other branch of the hospital, but when we did, we were further dismayed to hear that Ros would have to be admitted on to a ward before she could receive her treatment. Everything seemed to move at a snail's pace, as we tried to persuade the staff that once Ros had had her injection she would be fine to leave. After three hours, a freeze-dried concentrate of factor VIII was injected and we left, but it was well after midnight when we reached our holiday home again. It had been an unnerving and exhausting experience.

We found out later that the Haemophilia Society were well aware of the differences between haemophilia centres. The best ones provided full, comprehensive management and home treatment therapy. There were some who merely provided treatment infusions and very little else in the way of care. This could be partly due to the fact that some centres only had a handful of patients, so it was difficult for them to run an effective comprehensive service. In small hospitals there might only be one haematologist, so there would be problems if he or she were away. It was apparently not unknown for a consultant in charge of a haemophilia centre to like the distinction of running such a centre, but not the responsibility of taking proper care of the patients. In all but the largest of the centres, haemophilia care was linked with leukaemia care, as haematologists look after both. This was a disadvantage, because leukaemia patients were frequently terminally ill. Staff would understandably prioritise their needs, leaving the patients with haemophilia to get second best. Pendlebury had a very good leukaemia unit, but Dr Evans told me that he made sure it was separate from the haemophilia unit.

Throughout all the years that I left Ros in hospital and came home to care for the other members of the family, I felt a strange pull towards her. I cannot recollect when this feeling started, but I soon became aware that I felt joined to her by an invisible elastic thread. It would feel very taut as I went further away from her, only loosening again as I travelled back to be with her. When she was very young and vulnerable it was quite a strong sensation, only lessening as she gained more independence and as I felt less anxiety for her.

Ros never complained about having her treatment. She recognised that there were certain limits to her daily life, which sometimes frustrated her, but she was determined to carry on as normal and would hop or hobble about the house, getting things done. There were days when I was over anxious about her and other days when I did not want to summon up the energy to deal with a new situation, but I never denied that she had vWd.

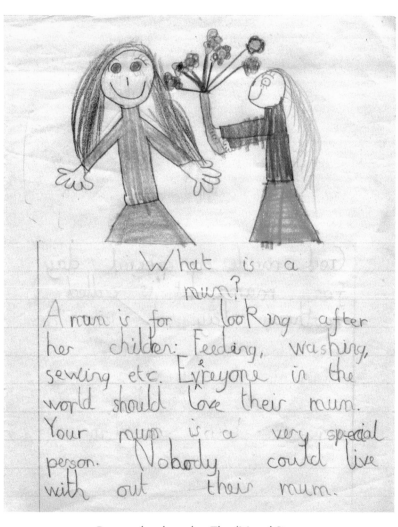

What is a mum?

A mum is for looking after her childer. Feeding, washing, sewing etc. Evreyone in the world should love their mum. Your mum is a very special person. Nobody could live with out their mum.

Ros – school work – The 'Mum' Story

Chapter Seven

Ros joined the junior school of Cheadle Hulme School in September 1982. Founded originally under the name of Warehousemen and Clerks in Victorian times, the impressive old red brick buildings of this independent day and boarding school stood in a leafy suburb of south Manchester, close to the main railway line in Cheadle Hulme. Gardens, tennis courts and a copse of trees set off the imposing structures of the school. New classroom blocks and a sports hall had been added in the grounds. To one side lay open sports fields and netball courts. On first impression this was all rather daunting.

Fortunately, the junior school was a new building on one level set at the far end of the grounds. Class numbers here were small and the children educated to a high standard, with the welfare of the whole child in mind, not just their academic achievement. The head of the junior school was a kind man, totally dedicated to his work and his staff team were capable and caring. As the whole school took boarding pupils as well as day pupils there was a fully staffed and equipped medical centre and sick bay, situated in the Victorian part of the school. We gave information on Ros's condition to all those who needed it and soon had a good rapport with the sister in charge of the small medical team. Whichever of them was on duty would phone us if Ros had any problems. When I learned that there were trained nurses on site I secretly hoped that supplies of factor VIII could be kept at school and administered by one of the nurses, but this was not offered.

There was an easy informality which meant that access to different areas of the school was not difficult. I soon felt comfortable walking through the medical centre to look for Ros. There she would be in one of the dingy rooms, resting on an old iron bedstead, covered by a pastel coloured crocheted blanket. She might be reading through a pile of old magazines if she felt well enough, clutching a bloodied tissue to her nose or mouth, or resting an injured limb. Over the years the nursing staff were very kind to Ros and very helpful to me. I think there were times when Ros just sloped off there for a rest.

The attitude of the school towards her was supportive, especially when she was on crutches or in her wheelchair. The junior school was easily accessible, but the dining hall for all pupils, senior and junior, was upstairs in the main building. Ros was allowed to use the service lift to get up there for her lunch; also to wait in the library for me to pick her up after school. If Ros was in her wheelchair, it was not unknown for a teacher to swap a whole class into another classroom at ground level, in order to accommodate her.

I maintained an interest in all matters to do with adoption. I wrote an article for the British Agencies for Adoption and Fostering quarterly journal (Volume 7 no 4 1983) entitled *Late discovery of medical problems*. It described how we discovered Ros's medical condition after we had adopted her and how we had largely had to educate ourselves about von Willebrand's disease. It was to be a couple more years before we joined the national network of adoptive parents, 'Parent to Parent Information on Adoption Service' (PPIAS), now known as Adoption UK. A small group of adoptive parents, struggling with issues around adoption, had first met around a kitchen table in the home of an adoptive mother in London. The group grew rapidly as a supportive body for families experiencing problems, who were not receiving any post-adoption support from their local authorities. We found PPIAS to be most helpful, especially the national meetings and conferences, as well as articles about people's experiences of adoption in the quarterly journals.

We were having difficulty in coping with Paul's very controlling behaviour. He wanted the last word in any discussion, he could be very manipulative and he was over-active, all traits of someone lacking attachment to a care giver. I had read John Bowlby's book, *Child Care and the Growth of Love* in the sixties and understood what negative effects the lack of bonding between mother and baby could have. James Robertson's work had also highlighted the anxiety caused by separation of parent and child. Through our contact with PPIAS we learned about holding therapy, which had first been tried with autistic children. A pilot project was due to start and we asked if we could be included. We were accepted and travelled to London once a week for eight weeks for this controversial therapy. Over the weeks of this experimental treatment we noticed small changes in Paul's behaviour, but he was still a demanding, over-excited and difficult little boy. We followed up other avenues of help and therapy during the next few years, but with little success. In the mid 1990's PPIAS set up a support network for parents like us, struggling to keep going with our care of our emotionally damaged children.

Meanwhile, Ros's aches, pains and small bleeds continued unabated. In 1982 Dr Evans decided that she should have X-rays of her main joints, to see if there was any damage from these bleeds. The result that they looked all right and seemed healthy was reassuring. She was very long suffering about wearing the proper footwear while she was young, although I knew she really wanted something a little trendier like her friends. Poor Ros, I was always buying boring sensible shoes for her, so that her ankles and feet would remain healthy. However, a year after these X-rays, both ankles were X-rayed again at the review clinic and her right ankle now showed some signs of arthritis. Despite the pain that Ros suffered in her feet and ankles, she continued to be most resilient and in 1983 she walked fifteen miles on the school's charity hike. This was a well organised sponsored event that the school arranged each year, in aid of one local, one national and one international charity. There were regular

Ros and Paul, with friend's dog
on the Cheadle Hulme School Charity Hike

check points and plenty of responsible adults to oversee the walkers. Ros completed this long walk with no adverse effects.

With my hectic lifestyle, as mother of two children making demands on me, I was feeling quite stressed by my situation. My health began to suffer. I was often extremely tired, but put this down to all the running around I was doing. I consulted my GP who did a blood test. I was found to be anaemic and he prescribed iron pills to correct this. An incident, in November 1983, illustrates how difficult life could be.

Ros's ankle had been playing up a lot and there came a day when Dr Evans said that she should rest it for a week. It was getting towards the end of the long autumn term, Ros was tired and the announcement upset her. However, we were trying to be firm with her and had managed to get to school and to all her other commitments with the help of the wheelchair. I had seen a gynaecologist because of my anaemia and had been advised to have an investigative D and C. I was due in hospital for this minor operation the day before Paul's eighth birthday. Because of this, we had decided to have a small birthday party for Paul on the Sunday prior to my hospital visit.

As we prepared for the party that day, Ros was supposed to be resting her foot but we were having difficulty keeping her seated in one place. Paul was 'high' with excitement, his friends due at any moment. Then Ros's nose started to bleed. It was obvious that she would need treatment. The usual trick of pinching the nostrils firmly together to stop the bleeding was not working. Ros was sitting with her head over a bowl, dripping blood and there was general chaos. Paul's friends began to arrive for the party. We phoned for an ambulance, which came very quickly. The kind paramedic was reassuring and said that all I needed to do was to pinch Ros's nostrils and the bleeding would soon stop. (We always did this but it never worked.) He kindly proceeded to demonstrate as we sped through Manchester at high speed with siren blaring. I looked rather foolish when we arrived at Pendlebury and the bleeding had stopped, but Ros had a very sore nose! However, she was kept in overnight as the bleeding re-occurred and the doctors decided to keep an eye on her.

Back at home the party was kept going by Veronica and Daniel, who finished off the sandwich making and helped John to keep the children entertained. Later, Daniel came to fetch me home. I felt exhausted, anxious, fed up and not in the party mood. Poor Paul. Next day I had to phone the two hospitals, first Stepping Hill, our local hospital, to see if there was a bed for me, then the children's hospital to check on Ros's progress overnight and to let them know where I would be. I went off for my two night stay with a heavy heart and in a state of anxiety. I did not want to put off my operation as I had waited months for it and my tiredness and general debility were continuing. All was well that evening. John fetched Ros from Pendlebury and brought both children in to visit me. I was seeing too much of the inside of hospitals and was feeling miserable.

Early in 1984 Ros was measured for a leg splint, which the physiotherapist at Pendlebury thought might help with her aches and pains. This splint was made of strong white plastic and fitted round the ankle and foot, fastening with Velcro straps. She had to wear it inside her shoe. It was useful for a while, but Ros found it rather uncomfortable, as her foot was held in one position. As she was growing fast it was soon too small and was not replaced.

At the next review clinic Dr Evans referred Ros to an ENT specialist. He was concerned about her frequent nosebleeds. All the bleeds had weakened the tiny blood vessels in her nose, so on this visit Ros had to have some of them cauterized. This was a very unpleasant experience for a nine year old. It involved the specialist heating up a long skewer type implement and then inserting this red-hot needle up her nose to seal the damaged blood vessel.

She continued to have gum bleeds from time to time with the last of the baby teeth coming out. As each tooth went, as well as going on our round trip of the hospitals we had to ensure that she only ate soft food for a few days, so as not to restart any bleeding.

Paul sat the entrance exam for Cheadle Hulme junior school and was successful. We were all thrilled at this; seeing the care Ros was getting, as well as the smaller class sizes, encouraged us to hope that Paul would settle in.

It may appear that life did very much centre around Ros, with trips to hospital and other appointments, which were very time consuming, but both children had good social contacts and enjoyed a variety of activities. With Ros's wider circle of friends, she had to be picked up from further afield in the evenings or at weekends. All her friends' parents were told a little about von Willebrand's, and they could phone me if anything were to occur while Ros was in their care. Despite all the friendships that Ros made, I think she was teased at school. Children tease if they think someone might be the odd one out. After a school trip to Chester one day, Ros was very upset in the evening and said that she felt that she was not normal. Maybe it was this that spurred her into showing everyone how normal she was. With some of her friends and John and Paul, Ros again tackled fifteen miles of the Cheadle Hulme charity hike. This year she came back with swollen, hurting ankles and had to have treatment.

There was a national increase in the number of haemophiliacs suffering bouts of infective jaundice from hepatitis viruses. More than in any other age group children between the ages of five and fourteen were suffering from jaundice and there was debate about this unusual rise. A new form of hepatitis was spreading in the USA and there was speculation that this was affecting patients with haemophilia in the UK, because of the concentrate they received for their treatment. The newer cases of acute hepatitis were neither hepatitis A nor hepatitis B and were therefore called non-A non-B. The introduction of a vaccine for hepatitis B prevented that particular disease in the haemophilia population and Ros was duly immunised. But it was now reported to us that she carried the non-A non-B virus in her bloodstream. Nothing was known about it and there was no information to worry us at this stage.

Another virus was creating concern for people with haemophilia. Eleven out of 20,000 haemophiliacs in the USA had developed Acquired Immune Deficiency Syndrome (AIDS) caused by the Human Immunodeficiency Virus (HIV). Worry was growing that a new factor VIII treatment, concentrated from a pool of donors, might be helping the spread of this disease, since it only needed one donor with AIDS to infect the entire pool. Doctors were taking the risks seriously, as over half the factor VIII used in Britain was imported from the USA. We were not too worried about Ros contracting AIDS as she was still receiving cryo, so the risk to her was minimal.

One bizarre incident, however, springs to mind, which occurred because of the increased interest and worry over AIDS. We went for a routine visit to the dental hospital and had to wait longer than usual. When Ros's turn came I was somewhat astonished to find the treatment area looking very alien. The dentist looked like a spaceman and we could hardly see her through the layers of protective clothing. Much of the area surrounding the chair where Ros was to sit was protected by plastic covers and the whole place had been made as sterile as possible. The appointment went on as usual, but there was an atmosphere I did not like. I felt it was an insult, a suggestion that Ros was somehow unclean and that precautions were being taken because Ros was a bleeder, even though there was no evidence to suggest that she had HIV. I was upset by this incident, which was not repeated to this extent. We still wanted to know more about AIDS however, and both John and I went to different meetings held at Pendlebury to hear the latest information.

Since the shortage of treatment in the 1970's there had been a push to get the UK self-sufficient in its production of blood products. More patients were going on to home treatment so there was an increase in demand for blood products. The Haemophilia Society kept close scrutiny on developments at Elstree, where the new Blood Products Laboratory was being built. We, as society members, were assured through *The Bulletin* that the UK would be self-sufficient by the end of 1986. The centre opened in April 1987.

Developments at Pendlebury since Ros's diagnosis were encouraging. Dr Evans had set up one of the first haemophilia centres for children in the country. By 1977, he decided that he needed a nurse specialist to look after the children that he was seeing who had haemophilia and other bleeding disorders. It was at a time when specialist nurses were starting to become part of a nursing team, but they were few and far between. People were realising that in some areas like cancer care, it was necessary to have a nurse who specifically specialised in that area.

Sister Alex Shaw had been a surgical nurse before taking time out to have a family. She wanted to return to work at Pendlebury as a theatre sister. Her employers were very far-sighted and, at her interview, offered her the post of working with Dr Evans as a nurse specialist in haemophilia care. She was told about Dr Evans's search for a haemophilia nurse specialist and agreed to take the job. When Alex was appointed the matron informed her that they did not know what the job entailed. "We don't even know what this job with haemophilia is; it's what you make it," she said. This was very daunting for Alex; nobody understood what was required, least of all her.

Dr Evans was not sure how the other centres around the country had developed, so he and Alex visited centres at Newcastle and Oxford. He gave her books to read and told her to go off and study, saying, "Learn about blood and blood clotting and everything else to do with blood". He wanted Alex to educate people, to teach and to speak publicly on this subject which was so new to her. Alex took up the challenge and became the haemophilia nurse specialist.

Soon the haemophilia centre had a proper treatment room. Though small, this room was better than a row of chairs in the path lab corridor and Dr Evans's tiny laboratory. The haemophilia room was situated on the corner of two corridors in the main building, next to the admissions unit which delivered the haemophilia treatments at night and after hours. The room was not big enough for all the work that was carried out but it gave recognition to the importance of that work. The room housed a treatment bed, a couple of chairs, shelving piled high with reference books and toys, a sink, a fridge and loads of boxes of supplies. With people in, it was overcrowded. Nevertheless any staff who had worked under the previous cramped conditions were delighted with it. On the wall was a list of all the children who attended; some were getting stars on charts for coping well with their injections. Pictures drawn by some of the children were displayed for all to see and a friendly atmosphere pervaded this room. It was in this room that Alex started her excellent work treating, educating and always reassuring her young patients and their families. We did not know at the time that she was learning on the job. She displayed assurance with authority and kindness. She was sensitive to every need and she particularly sympathised with the young girls in her care, having two daughters of her own. As the service expanded another sister, Jenny Cryer, was appointed; everyone called her Sister Cryo!

Waiting at the hospital took up a large part of our visits. The waiting area for the haemophilia room was on the main hospital corridor and identified only by a row of chairs. Here we sat and watched the hospital world go by as we waited for our turn. We often saw people we knew, nurses from Borchardt ward or doctors who had come into contact with Ros. Sometimes they sped by, bent on some important mission, but occasionally they stopped to ask after Ros and to chat. Time and again we met the same families waiting for their appointment and the parents could chat and compare notes. Ros was very friendly and found other children to talk to or play with and there were a few toys available, but we learned early on that it was as well to take toys or books with us to while away the long hours. Ros worked at homework if she felt up to it or if we were not mopping up her bleeding.

The main corridor was home to a number of larger-than-life-size stuffed donkeys and rocking horses, which had seen better days, but children still clambered on them. We often stopped to admire 'Gnasher', the large piranha fish in a tank, whose feeding time, like the animals in the zoo, was at a regular hour. Friends of Pendlebury Hospital often had stalls for selling new or second-hand items. I still found waiting a very tedious process; I often let my mind go blank and would stare intently at pictures or notices on the wall, reading and re-reading them past the point of boredom. I could glance at an old magazine but not concentrate on it. Waiting became a state of mind – there was rarely any impatience attached to it; it was just something we had to get through. Wound up with the cares of the day, I would let the cocooning atmosphere of the hospital drift around me until our turn came. After the appointment was over, we would refresh ourselves with tea and Penguin biscuits in the Womens' Voluntary Service (WVS) canteen. Our special treat was cheese toasties, as a little reward for having to spend time at the hospital.

Paul's behaviour still gave rise to much concern, though now that he was also in the junior school at Cheadle Hulme, we knew he was getting a better level of care and understanding. Ros was successful in passing the exam for the senior school. Her independence was growing and she was becoming much more adept at recognising her bleeds and knowing when she might need treatment. The school staff were coping excellently and she was able to go on trips and educational visits without one of us tagging along, though I had to be at home or on the end of a phone somewhere, on call.

Ros's social activities were keeping her busy. She was not put off by the interruptions, caused by her bleeds, to these various interests and was able to take a full part in them. Kitty and Ros, for some time active with the brownies, now became the first members of a new guide troop. She had started having cello lessons at school and passed her Grade 2 exam. She joined the Maia girls' choir in Stockport and participated in local Quaker events organised for children.

In 1986 one of these Quaker events was a five day stay in a hostel in the grounds of an historic Quaker Meeting House at Yealand, near Carnforth. Ros wanted to go. While she was on trips locally nearer home, with school or the guides, we could be on call. This was to be further afield, so we explored the possibility of staying somewhere nearby. A hotel or bed and breakfast were out of the question, as financially our budget was tight with paying two sets of school fees. The north west group of the Haemophilia Society had a caravan at Caton on the river Lune near Lancaster which could be hired for a small fee. It was about ten miles from Yealand, so was ideal. We booked our few days there and when the time came, we left Ros with her friends, giving clear instructions to the helpers as to what to do in an emergency. This was a somewhat risky arrangement on our part, as we still did not have a mobile phone. We gave the helpers the number of the owner of the caravan site and hoped that all would be well. As it was Easter time, the weather was still quite chilly. We shivered through the few cold nights in the caravan, which was warmed by the sun during the day. Ros enjoyed her time at Yealand and was able to join in all the walks, games and activities without mishap. Alas, our first stress free holiday break was clouded by the death of John's mother. On our return from Lancaster we had to travel straight to Bath for the funeral.

During the 1980's vWd was classified, and the disease was described as severe, moderate or mild. The diagnosis of vWd had been made on the basis of low factor VIII levels, coupled with a long bleeding time. Most patients were regarded as severe sufferers.

When more sophisticated laboratory tests came along, minor abnormalities noticed in the laboratory could be used to identify mild cases, whose bleeding history was varied and inconstant. The classification into severe, moderate or mild was based on clinical symptoms, but the history of these classifications is difficult for the layman to understand. By the 1980's the types of vWd, 1, 2a and 2b and type 3, were recognised. The condition is now described under these headings.

The vWd factor is a blood protein that acts like a glue, helping the platelets in the blood to stick to the blood vessels that are damaged. Lack of vWd factor in the blood means that the platelets will not stick together properly, to form a plug at the site of the bleeding, so there is a prolonged bleeding time as clot formation is slow. In type 1, the mildest and most common form of vWd, the patient has low levels of the vWd factor, but it functions normally. Three in every four people with vWd have type 1, and 1% of the UK population have it. People with 2a have a large amount of vWd factor, but it does not work properly, so this type is classed as moderate. In 2b the disorder is characterised by thrombocytopenia, which is a low platelet count, and is classed as moderate to severe. Ros suffers from type 3 which is classified as severe and is the rarest form of the condition, affecting between one and five in a million people in the UK. The vWd factor is usually lacking altogether and the patient also has low amounts of clotting factor VIII. (Proof to us that Ros is one in a million!) Our understanding of the condition continued to develop as time went by.

As Ros grew older there were longer gaps between the hospital visits and for a time we could forget her condition and carry on a more normal existence. But worse was yet to come. In 1987 she began to experience some very severe bleeding, when her periods began.

Extract from a family holiday diary,
Yorkshire, August 1985, describing a walk to Gaping Gill Hole

After lunch we put on our hiking boots and set of on a rather long and tiring walk up to the 'gaping gil'. On the way up to it I had to stop quite a few times. But luckily mom waited with me. On the way up, it was mostly steep uphills with a few levels and I think two, in all, small places going downwards.

On the way up mum kept saying that she thought they sold chocolate etc. on the top. This was really a joke because she was going to provide it herself.

On the top it was very boggy and when Paul was jumping across one patch he landed splatch!, in it. At the pothole, the gil, I had a banana and everyone had two peices of chocolate. Yum Yum! When I had had my banana I threw the skin down into the pothole.

It was more easy coming down the hill and we arrived back at home in good time. Thats all for now. I'll be seeing you! Bye. ⑱

Chapter Eight

In discussion with Alex Shaw over writing this book, when we began to talk about menstruation, she said, "The worst time for girls with bleeding disorders is puberty – it's hell!" Women's bleeding, menstruation, periods or "the curse" as it was known in my day, is still a taboo subject, very private to women and not often written about or discussed, except in the medical profession. Though these days there are articles in women's magazines, thousands of women have problems with their periods and struggle on in silence with pain and heavy bleeding, thinking that it is normal. It is known that vWd in any form now affects one in a hundred people; many of these will be undiagnosed women with bad periods who are coping the best way they can without help.

1987 started much as the previous years with life's ups and downs. Cheadle Hulme School advised us that Paul was not likely to be accepted into the senior school and he was assessed as having special educational needs by the local authority. They would prepare a statement of those needs in due course. His over-active behaviour, which could disrupt the school day, added to the stresses already in place with the trips to hospital. We were having visits from an educational psychologist whom I had met once or twice at Charnwood. We were looking into the possibility of sending Paul to a special school, Breckenbrough, which only offered boarding facilities. My conscience was telling me that this would not be a good idea, as Paul might see this as a further rejection of him by parental figures.

I had been to see the gynaecologist again, as I was experiencing heavy bleeding and pain each month and felt very weary at this time. I was due to have a hysterectomy at Stepping Hill Hospital.

Ros was getting on well at school and enjoying all that she was doing. She often had nights away or sleep overs, as they were known, with her friends. One day in June Ros, now aged thirteen, started her first period. It was a day I had secretly been dreading, though I tried not to let her know of my worry and had talked to her about it 'all being very normal'. She knew that I was having trouble with my periods and was sympathetic, but maybe did not understand the full implications.

For the first three days she bled heavily, but coped well. On the fourth day she woke looking grey and ill and had a temperature of 102°C. We went to Pendlebury, where a doctor said that she had a virus. No treatment was given and thankfully her temperature was down to 99°C by the evening. The next day she was still bleeding profusely and when this had not abated by the following morning we went back to the hospital, where treatment was given and a blood count taken. This proved to be low, so Ros was booked in for a blood transfusion. She was looking pale and washed out by this time. The transfusion took ages to be set up and Ros spent a long day at the hospital, finally getting home with me at 11.00pm. But she looked pink instead of white, which was a relief.

While all this was going on, I had heard from Stepping Hill who wanted me in hospital for my operation the day following Ros's transfusion, so I was doubly relieved that she was over the worst. I had made so many plans for my absence that I went into hospital feeling fairly confident. I was in hospital for twelve days. I had a slow recovery at home over the next six weeks. Family, friends and neighbours all rallied round, doing small jobs for me. On one of my first trips out, Ros walked me up and down the road!

As soon as the summer term ended we packed up to go to Wales. Ros was going on the North Wales adventure holiday, organised by the Haemophilia Society and was joining a crowd of twenty-five haemophilic boys. She would be the only girl! The haemophilia centre at Bangor was to provide cover for the children if treatment was needed. The team of helpers included staff from some of the other treatment centres and they were able to give injections at any time or in any place. The base for all these activities was Cornelyn Manor, an outdoor pursuits centre near Beaumaris on Anglesey. Canoeing, gorge walking, rock climbing and abseiling were all on the agenda. In my still weak state, post op, I was concerned that Ros might not cope with these rather strenuous pursuits. I was reassured when we reached Anglesey, met some of the staff and realised that she was actually looking forward to engaging in some of these 'banned' activities. I admired her spirit. We left her happily making friends with some of the boys and went to mid-Wales for the week, to stay in a guest-house owned by some friends. I enjoyed the rest, and

John and Paul went off on outings, which I joined when I felt able. At the end of the week we went to fetch Ros from Anglesey. As soon as she saw us she dissolved in tears and said how much she would miss everyone. She had had a great time and was none the worse for all her adventures.

The day after we returned home, Ros started her second period. She was tired from the activity holiday, but became droopy and miserable too, and did not want to go to the local guide camp. We eventually persuaded her to go, only to have to fetch her home the next day. After 24 hours rest she went back to the camp. After a further eleven days of bleeding, I took her for treatment but this did not stop the continuous flow.   All this time Ros was coping extremely well with a stoicism that I was proud of. She certainly was not going to be beaten by this new complication in her life. A few days later she went off to Quaker summer school, this time without me, but with copious instructions and notes for the helpers. On her return a week later she was still bleeding, so yet more treatment was given. Ros did not appear to be anaemic, even after three weeks of bleeding. We decided to go ahead with our next plan for this summer, a holiday in Devon.

We had booked a cottage in a village near Sidmouth and were sharing it with John's brother, Christopher, and his family for a week. This cottage was charming; it was an old dairy house and was roomy enough for the two families and well equipped. There was a big garden for the children to explore. The following incident sticks in my mind because to this day I'll never know why I did not act sooner. We had planned a visit to my aunt, Isabel, on our first day at the cottage. She lived in a village some miles along the coast and, as my father was spending a few days with her, we thought it would be nice to see them both. That morning, Ros complained of period pain in her stomach, which was not unusual, but by the time we reached Aunty's house she did not seem well and needed to lie down. Aunt Isabel, who prided herself on being an expert in childcare, fussed over Ros and put her to bed with a hot water bottle for comfort. The rest of us went out for a walk to the nearby beach, but on our return Ros was no better. During our drive back to the cottage later on, Ros suddenly shouted, "Stop the car! Stop the car! I can't bear it!" The pain was getting much worse with the movement of the car aggravating it. John stopped the car on a grass verge. Ros and I got out and breathed in some fresh air. Back at the cottage, she retired to bed again; when she did not come down to watch her favourite TV programme, I knew I must take action. Her pain was obviously too bad to ignore, and why I had not seen this earlier I will never know. We phoned the doctor on call at the cottage hospital in Sidmouth who suggested that we took Ros to see him. He was most kind and thorough, but could not help and recommended that we go to the Royal Devon and Exeter Hospital (R D and E) at Wonford, Exeter. He gave us good directions and we set off on the fifteen mile journey. On arrival at the R D and E, the duty doctors examined Ros and listened while we spoke of her history of bleeds. They decided that she must stay overnight as there was a possibility she had some internal bleeding. She was admitted to a ward and when she seemed settled we left her to rest. It was 1.15am when we finally returned to our lovely holiday home, feeling tired and gloomy.

Our holiday cottage in Devon
l-r: Margaret, Christopher, Ros, Linda, John, Juliet, Philip,
Paul, Jennifer (in shade)

Next day, we went back to see Ros as soon as we could. The treatment given to her after we left had caused an allergic reaction. She had come out in a blotchy red rash. She was smothered in calamine lotion to soothe the swelling and itchiness and, by the time we saw her, the rash had disappeared. Her pain and bleeding were coming under control, but she was found to be anaemic, so was set up for a blood transfusion that evening. I stayed with her all day; John and Paul went off to look round Exeter and visited the Maritime Museum. Fortunately, Ros was well enough to leave hospital on the third day.

The nearest beach at Exmouth drew us to it; it was a lovely summer day and Ros paddled in the sea. We did not know what had caused the intense pain, but assumed it was some internal bleeding which had now stopped. A few days of normal holiday activities – walks, picnics and trips to the beach – helped to restore our spirits, but our holiday had been affected by Ros's problem. The others recorded in the guest book that it had clouded what would otherwise have been a happy week together. We never stayed there again, although it was such a lovely place.

On our return home, we asked Dr Evans to check Ros over. He thought that she might have had a urinary infection and wanted to treat her with antibiotics. The notes had not come through from R D and E, so he had to rely on what we could tell him. Ros, now feeling a lot better, went off with her best friend, Kitty, to help as guides with the brownies at their camp in Derbyshire.

Towards the end of August we had news of Paul's schooling. The educational psychologist was pushing on with his reports and we were invited to go on a day visit to Breckenbrough School near Thirsk in Yorkshire. I knew this school from many years before, when I had been invited to spend a weekend there in an advisory capacity. I liked the sound of it now, knowing that it was a school with Quaker governors and a high ratio of staff to pupils. Although it was further from home than I would have liked, it seemed important that Paul, with his many abilities, should get a decent education, along with help and support for his emotional problems. Breckenbrough was to play a vital part in our lives over the next few years and was very supportive of Paul and of us, too. We were gradually getting over the events of the summer and looking forward to the new term. Paul needed new clothes and other items for his new school, so there was shopping to do.

By the middle of September Ros had started her third period. With her previous experiences still so close I was hoping that things might settle down. This proved not to be the case and was the start of an autumn and winter where Ros spent long weeks in hospital.

But before we were caught up in this next lot of trauma, I took Paul to start at Breckenbrough. It was a day of sunshine and showers, "a bright day" as Paul described it, as we drove north up the A1. Rainbows appeared in the clouded sky, not just one but many, one following another as we travelled. I felt they were a good omen, something bright and colourful to remember, on a day when I was bottled up with anxiety. Paul had a warm welcome at the school and I left him looking very cheerful. On my return journey I pulled into a lay-by halfway home and had a good cry. I felt so guilty at leaving him.

Despite having cryo on the ninth day of heavy bleeding, this third period was as bad as the others. Ros was so determined to carry on normally that on the fifteenth day of bleeding she bravely walked eleven and a half miles of the fifteen mile Cheadle Hulme hike, before being picked up by John. Although she sat on her jacket, the car seat was stained with blood, her bleeding was so relentless. On the seventeenth day we were back at the hospital. Ros's blood count was down to 8.7 so she went in for a transfusion the following day. By now she was white and shaky, with no natural reserves of energy. Once home again after the transfusion she was awake with pain and bleeding most of the night. The next day she passed large clots of blood about every half an hour. Once again we went back to the hospital where Ros's blood count was found to be even lower than before. So much for the transfusion! This time she was kept in Pendlebury for four days. Following a second blood transfusion, while I was not there, Ros got out of bed and masses of blood gushed out from under her nightie onto the floor. It was very frightening. Dr Evans quickly contacted a gynaecology colleague, a professor, who recommended a low dose hormone pill for Ros and this was prescribed immediately. Daily doses of cryo and another blood transfusion were given and at last Ros began to recover.

While she stayed in hospital Ros was asked to help with the medical students' exams, and earned £10. They asked questions to try and determine what her medical condition was ... most were stumped!

Back at home Ros still felt very tired and did not feel like going to school. She had missed large chunks of her education in this early part of the term. Though she had done some bits of work for the teacher on the ward, her school work was disrupted, so we were all surprised by Ros's end of year report. This stated, *"I am impressed by the level-headed way in which Rosamund has confronted the problems caused by absence. She has a very positive attitude which is reflected in the creditable marks she achieved in many of her examinations".*

Following Dr Evans's contact with the professor of gynaecology at Withington Hospital, we soon had an appointment. It was to be our first visit back there since our initial appointment with Ros as a baby, when she had had the heel prick and the first signs of abnormal bleeding. After giving Ros an internal examination Prof, as everyone called him, told us her uterus was very enlarged and had something 'alien' in it, as he described it. He told us that he wanted to do a D and C and a laparoscopy very soon, to discover what this might be. We were all shattered by this announcement. I was very worried. A few weeks went by in which Ros was able to return to normal life and attend school. We went back to Prof's clinic for preliminary tests, before Ros's admission to Withington, on an adult women's ward the following Sunday, for her operation on the Monday. Factor VIII cover had been arranged in consultation with Pendlebury and this was to start overnight prior to the operation. On the Monday Ros had her minor investigative surgery and recovered well. Prof came round to the ward to speak to us about the results of his investigations. He announced that Ros had masses of tiny cysts on her ovaries, which were enlarged and that this was most likely due to an hormonal imbalance. This was a great relief, as we assumed that this could be rectified and controlled by drug treatment. Little did we realise that the procedures, though very minor, were to be the cause of much more internal bleeding.

We did not know at the time but months later, Alex told me about

Mittelschmerz syndrome. During ovulation when the egg comes out of the ovary and starts to go down the fallopian tube, in women with vWd, it sometimes starts to bleed, causing a lot of pain. Quite often it is mistaken for appendicitis in women who do not have a bleeding problem. The pain is very severe, causing the patient to double up. I wondered if this had happened to Ros in Devon.

I had developed great trust in the care that Ros received at Pendlebury; they understood her bleeds and treated her accordingly. This new form of bleeding was less well understood and, although Prof was in close touch with Dr Evans regarding her factor VIII back up, I began to have doubts as to whether Ros's condition was properly understood by Prof and his team of specialists. I had experienced her suffering for a dozen years. I knew what her bleeding episodes were like. I had seen what could happen even after a blood transfusion. I wanted to say to the doctors, "Whatever you do and however careful you are, she will still bleed".

Following the D and C and laparoscopy Ros continued to have intermittent abdominal pain. We called the on-call doctor on three different occasions but each one in turn could not explain it. They did not say, "Go to your hospital," and we did not know what to do. Ros stayed off school. She had some good days and some bad days. For some while she had been trying to earn some pocket money by doing a paper round. All the time she was off John would go and do it for her, sometimes with help from Paul or from me. It was extra for John on top of a busy college day. Paul was able to come home for a weekend occasionally. I was glad of this, but also relieved that he was unaffected by the disruption to home life that occurred during these few months.

Prof decided that Ros should have an ultrasound scan two weeks after her operation. Unfortunately, when this was done, it showed a mass of blood in her abdomen and Ros was immediately re-admitted to hospital for observation. The blood was thought to be infected, so she was given a course of antibiotics. No wonder she was in so much pain! Three days later a further scan showed that the mass of blood was larger. There was evidence that the internal bleeding was continuing. Was all of this occurring because of the D and C and laparoscopy?

It looked as though Ros might be in hospital for some time. Prof decided to move her from the adult gynaecology ward to the newly built Duchess of York Children's Hospital, which adjoined Withington Hospital. This building was cheerful, fresh and clean compared to the old, rather shabby adult ward. Ros transferred to a pleasant six-bedded ward, one of several placed around the central nurses' station. There was a girl in the next bed who had suffered a badly broken leg in a car accident. She and Ros became the 'long stays' of the ward; other children came for a few nights and went away again.

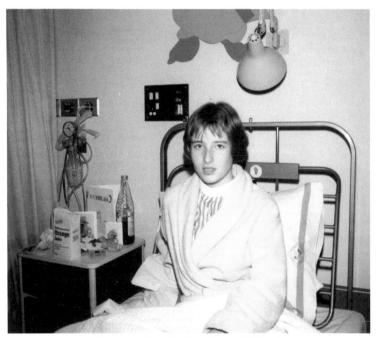

Ros confined to her hospital bed

Time dragged heavily for the two bed-bound girls. A hospital teacher brought them some schoolwork and Ros's teacher from Cheadle Hulme visited and brought some too. Ros often felt disinclined to do work and her days were much cheered by some of her friends visiting in the evenings. While I was doing my new job, escorting children to Charnwood during the day, I fitted in visits to Ros, to catch up with the latest developments on her health, to boost her morale and to bring fresh clothes and supplies of softer sanitary towels. (The ones issued by the hospital were cloth nappy like affairs!) Ros had a great need to feel clean. Having a warm, relaxing bath would have been helpful and soothing, but so often the water would be stained with blood, making the experience unpleasant. We were happier when we could go into the day room of the ward, very often with Kitty and her family, having takeaway suppers. Ros never enjoyed hospital food. Fortunately for her the nearby row of shops outside the hospital grounds housed an amazing assortment of takeaway restaurants, so we could vary the menu. We often patronised the hospital shop for sweets and magazines and bought snack meals at the bustling little restaurant along the corridor.

Looking back over this time, it is obvious that this was new territory for all of us – coping with severe menstrual bleeding, internal bleeds and the pain involved. I did not feel I could help Ros with the additional stresses and was relying too much on the doctors' knowledge and skill. Sometimes it seemed to me that they were baffled too. The 'hell' of puberty, described by Alex, was now upon us with all its inherent anxiety and worry. Ros did not understand what was happening to her body. Now being bleed free myself, I felt so sorry for her all the time. Her pain was something I experienced – sometimes as a true physical pain, other times real heartache for her condition. My recovery from the hysterectomy continued but the added strain of visiting Ros in hospital was taking its toll on my health. Tiredness, lack of energy and depression were part of my everyday life at this time. But I was so very proud of Ros, proud of the way she coped with her suffering and proud of the way she kept as positive as possible, given the ghastly things that were happening to her. Ros continued to stay in hospital. Over the next few days she had regular doses of cryo and needed yet another blood transfusion.

Prof's next decision was to try and draw off the blood from all the internal bleeding. She went to theatre to have a drain fitted. Poor Ros – this certainly was a strange piece of equipment that looked as if it had been created in the Dark Ages! It was a hollow tube of corrugated cardboard and it was inserted like a tampon, with a safety pin at the bottom to stop it from going any further inside her. The staff said that I could go down to theatre with her, where she had the contraption fitted, and sit with her when she came out into the recovery room. I wore a green gown and those blue plastic overshoes. I was able to hold Ros's hand and stroke her face and hair as she woke from the anaesthetic and as she felt her pain. She was very uncomfortable. It was distressing for me, but how much worse it was for her.

More scans and further bleeding ensued, but then Ros appeared to be recovering at last. She was given a date for coming home. Before she could, she had yet more heavy bleeding. Where was it all coming from and when was it all going to end? After this further setback and a total of two and a half weeks in hospital, she came home.

Ros had started on her hormone pill and was taking this regularly. It was designed to give a small bleed when the medication stopped. There had been some controversy over the pill as a birth control alternative as the long-term effects were not known. My mind was full of conflicting thoughts. On the one hand the anxiety of these long-term effects and on the other, relief that something had been found to control the bleeding. The pill was controlling her heavy periods; so, too, could it stop her conceiving. Withdrawing it would start the whole sorry process again and truthfully the thought of Ros having a baby in the future was not one I wished to contemplate.

Only six days after coming home from hospital Ros started her next period! By now it was two weeks before Christmas. We had had enough of hospitals for one year. Ros rested at home, making preparations for Christmas and seeing some of her friends. She was still only thirteen years old and had had experiences that would have traumatised an adult. Ros had shown great courage throughout all that was done to her. So ended 1987, our 'annus horribleedus' as Ros so succinctly put it!

Excerpt from Ros's blog, 15 August 2007
The Wrong Trousers

The White Trousers are indeed wrong – very wrong.

When I was a teenager going through period hell there are a number of incidents that remain indelibly etched in red in my rather shabby memory.

First was a sponsored walk that was organised by my school every year. You could choose whether you wanted to do the 5, 10 or 20 miles. I had previously done the 5 miles and although I couldn't walk for a week afterwards cos of ankle bleeds I was determined to do the 10 mile the next year with my friends.

However, dodgy joints apart, there was something different about me that year. I had hit puberty – like a truck full of ketchup ramming into a bridge support, there was red stuff everywhere. I was getting used to carrying masses of sanitary towels, feeling like I was in nappies again – and getting taken to the hospital for factor injections or blood transfusions every month.

Needless to say I was a bloody minded 13 year old and decided to enrol onto the 10 mile walk against my parents' better advice. With them assuring me that if I needed them I should get one of the marshalls, posted every few miles around the course, to give them a bell. I'm not going to need that I thought!

Off I set. I seem to remember it was a horrible day. Raining and windy and cold. I was wearing a very untrendy mac and hiking boots. Waterproof trousers would have been useful but I think I thought I was too cool for those – yeh, in that mac!

The course is so designed that there are toilets situated fairly regularly – either public or private at people's houses, opened just for the day of the walks. I used them all. I was no more than two thirds of the way round when I ran out of towels. And I'd taken plenty, I'd thought. I didn't want to give up so I kept going. Walking in the rain. Getting wetter.

It wasn't long before I was aware that my 'nappy' was feeling more and more sodden. I felt uncomfortably duck like in my gait, with a waddle and a bulky posterior. I kept walking. Trying to ignore the leaking sensation, less of a leak, more of a deluge by now.

At the next checkpoint I gave in and asked the marshall to ring my dad. When he arrived I had to use my mac as a seat covering to protect it from the blood that was flooding through my jeans. Dad drove a defeated daughter home.

Chapter Nine

The experience of Ros bleeding so badly had horrified me. It was nothing like my experience of heavy periods, which had been bad enough, or the experience of any one else I knew. This was much more extreme, almost life threatening, and it gave me great worries for Ros's future. Internal bleeding could be very dangerous and was hard to detect. She had coped so well with all that was done to her; she had put up with the pain and discomfort she so often experienced with a tenacity quite remarkable for a girl of her age. Of course there were times when she was moody or irritable, but she was now a teenager. It was difficult to tell whether her bad moods were due to the new hormone pill she took or normal adolescent behaviour. Certainly loud pop music assailed our ears and we could never get through Sunday tea-time each week without the top 40! In lots of ways our life returned to normality after this bad patch. Paul was settled at Breckenbrough and was able to have occasional weekends at home and sometimes we spent a day with him in Yorkshire.

Ros became accustomed to her new pill taking regime. When she stopped taking the pills for three days each month the bleeds were less heavy, but she still suffered a lot of pain.

In the spring, after one particularly prolonged session of pain I took Ros to our GP, who assumed, from her description of intense pain while on the toilet, that she had a urinary infection. She was given some antibiotics. A week later the pain was no better and we sought advice from Dr Evans, who prescribed Ponstan, an anti-inflammatory pain relief. Another week went by and the pain was still there. We consulted Dr Evans again and this time he thought that an ultrasound scan would be advisable, but Pendlebury did not have an appointment for three weeks! I could not bear the thought of Ros continuing in pain for that long. I wanted some action. Although Ros said she could handle it, I could not cope with her suffering all the time. Within two days I had managed to get her an appointment to see Prof. After seeing him a scan was done next day. This showed that Ros had been developing a massive internal bleed, a haematoma, about eight centimetres wide, the size of an apple. She was called back for a ten day stay in hospital, for rest, treatment and further scans until this enormous bleed had reduced in size. No wonder that she had been in pain.

Throughout the rest of this year Ros continued to have regular ultrasound scans to check that the internal bleeds had subsided. She was still having bad period pains but was coming to terms with them much better and, with the continuing use of Ponstan, was coping. At school all the teachers were pleased at how well Ros had caught up with her work. She had borrowed some of her friends' books to help her with this and had put in much effort. Soon, Prof announced that she was clear of internal bleeds and, after giving her a complicated new pill taking schedule, said that he did not want to see her for a year!

I wrote an article for the Haemophilia Society bulletin about vWd, about Ros and how we coped, accompanied by an informal snapshot of us all, taken in a hurry in our neighbour's back garden. I felt that the severe form of vWd warranted publicity. Articles, or references to it in any form, were sparse, even within the haemophilia community and I wanted it known that girls could suffer as well as boys.

One year at the Haemophilia Society AGM, we heard a talk given by the doctor in charge of the North Wales activity holiday, which Ros had attended. He spoke about all the activities the boys had engaged in, what enjoyment the boys had got out of the holiday and so on. All the time he was speaking I wanted to shout out, "But there was a girl there, too!" During the question time I made sure that Ros's presence on the holiday was acknowledged. However, it was plain to me that we had a long way to go in getting more recognition for female bleeders. If mentioned at all they were always passed off as being mildly affected and of no important significance. The doctor from North Wales rectified this later in the year when he showed his slides to the north west group at their AGM. We were pleased to see that Ros featured, wearing her life jacket and helmet. She had now been three times on this holiday and loved it. The young boy I had helped at Charnwood years ago also enjoyed some of these holidays. Tragically, he died a few years later, aged eighteen, of HIV infection, contracted through his contaminated NHS treatment.

I was beginning to get involved in the post adoption scene locally and had been at various meetings, planning to set up a post adoption centre in Manchester. Over the years our family had been woefully lacking any further support from the NCH; some support or help could have been useful throughout these years of struggle, with Ros's health and Paul's emotional problems. It was not for want of trying. On several occasions I had made contact with the north west agency, only to be told that they did not do adoptions any more. I found out some years later, while studying family placement on a course run by Manchester University, that in fact they *did* and one day a rather abashed social worker called on us, unannounced, to apologise for his agency's lack of response.

The Manchester Post Adoption centre would be the second of its kind in the country, the first being the well used Post Adoption Centre in London. I had been working at Charnwood for a number of years and now seemed the right time to move on. I had so much enjoyed working there. I had been very well supported through many crises and was sad to leave.

Ros was studying hard for her General Certificate of Secondary Education (GCSE) exams and revising started in earnest after a busy Easter holiday of activities. She was invited to have prophylactic treatment to see her through the weeks of the exams. This preventive treatment was such a relief. Just as the exams started we received a free radio pager, offered by a joint scheme between British Telecom (BT) and the Haemophilia Society. This pager gave us further peace of mind, knowing that Ros could contact us quickly if she needed to.

Following all this came another huge step for Ros and for all of us. She asked the team at Pendlebury if she could start doing her own injections. She was keen, having seen some of the boys on the adventure holidays doing their own jabs. I was not so sure; I wanted very much to support her, but I did not want to learn the process of injecting, should Ros fail at any time. I was scared I would damage her, make her bleed or inject an air bubble into her veins. How little faith I had in my own daughter – she took to it very well. The first two injections were done at the haemophilia clinic under supervision. We were so thrilled after she did her first one unaided at the hospital that we all went out for pizza to celebrate! I have never done an injection to this day. During the next couple of months whenever she needed treatment she practised doing her injections at the hospital, until the time came when she brought all the paraphernalia home.

During this summer holiday John was taken ill with suspected pancreatitis. He had been feeling unwell for several days staying in bed and refusing food and water. Our doctor sent him off to hospital, where he stayed for ten days and after various tests was found to have gallstones. Visiting him each day became difficult as our car broke down. I relied on John to look after all things to do with the car, so felt particularly helpless now. Luckily a good friend lent me her car to go to the hospital.

The day after John's return home from hospital Ros needed to do her first injection unsupervised. I was feeling very jaded that day. Paul was home for the holidays and he and I had argued the previous day, about smoking in the bathroom and he had disappeared all evening. I was anxious to know where he was, but was also helping John to settle back at home. When it got really late I called the police to see if they could track down my 12 year old, who might be wandering the streets. Eventually he came in at 1.00am.

John was restless all night long, after being in hospital, so I had had little sleep. I guess that Ros's anxiety levels were fairly high on this day, too and although I sat with her and talked her through the procedure, she could not get the needle into her vein this first injection at home. The next day we went to Pendlebury and Alex talked her through the whole process again, calmly and with great sensitivity.

After that, Ros became more confident each time she injected herself. It was so much more convenient for her, though it took time to prepare and draw up. Because the factor VIII was kept in the fridge, it had to be warmed up before being injected. The preparation, Haemate P, was a fine powder concentrate, contained in six bottles. To this was added sterile water drawn up by syringe from another six bottles. Once that was done we rolled the bottles, one at a time, between our hands to dissolve the concentrate thoroughly and to warm the product. It was then drawn up into a 50ml syringe and a butterfly needle was attached. Ros then fastened a tourniquet around one arm just above the elbow. This was tightened with the other hand and the selected vein was cleaned with a sterile swab. Generally she hit the vein first time every time. Ros had to fill in a form with the batch numbers of the factor VIII and the reason for the jab, and had to dispose of the needles into a 'sharps' bin.

The GCSE results came out. We were all delighted for Ros that, despite all her problems, she had received four A's, three B's and two C's!

Unbeknown to her, Ros had been nominated by the staff team at Pendlebury and selected by the Haemophilia Society together with two boys who had haemophilia, to represent them at the BBC Children of Courage event at Heathrow. She went on a Concorde flight with all the other nominees. Back at the airport, after various speeches, awards were given to the children who had won the Child of Courage prizes for that year. Ros did not receive one of these awards.

I really hoped that 1991 was going to be a successful and bleed free year for Ros and that things would improve generally for our family. Ros's internal bleeding had cleared and she was starting on work for her A levels. John had recovered well from his operation the previous autumn. I was working on the launch of the new post adoption centre in Manchester. Paul was still away at Breckenbrough and everything seemed settled for once.

Early in February Ros complained one day of pains and nausea and our GP again thought she might have a bladder infection. He was always very concerned for Ros

Paul riding a unicycle at Lightwater Valley

and on this occasion he called to see her the following Sunday morning. He had not ruled out the possibility that she might have appendicitis. Ros was not feeling any better, so he sent her to our local hospital where, after an examination, she was kept in for observation. We had always had it impressed upon us by the staff at Pendlebury that if there was any problem with Ros we should take her straight there, which we did, when she had obvious bleeding or swelling in a joint. Abdominal pain was another matter, though with her recent history and all the period pains I do not know why we did not insist that she go to Pendlebury. We had faith in our GP; he had been responsible for sending us off for the early tests before diagnosis, he had sent John quickly to hospital and he had cared for us all over the years.

After three days when nothing had been done, I had had enough. Ros's blood count was down, no scan had been done and the doctors were very undecided as to a diagnosis. I got her transferred to Pendlebury. Here, during a further two days a scan was done and it was found that Ros had another large abdominal bleed. She was sent home to rest and was to treat herself every day. At home she was poorly and uncomfortable, still experiencing bad pain.

After three more days I could not bear her to suffer any longer. I phoned Dr Evans who put a call through to Withington Hospital and we were given an appointment to see Prof the next day. He immediately admitted her and under anaesthetic the following morning inserted the awful corrugated contraption again, to try and draw off this mass of blood. A few days went by. A further scan was done. The abdominal mass looked just the same. Even the doctors were baffled. They continued treatment and eventually Ros improved enough to go home. February had been and gone. We had visited her in three different hospitals during the one month.

March was no better for Ros; the pains continued and so did the hospital visits, either to Pendlebury or Withington. When the pain became severe again she was re-admitted under Prof's care. After another week he was pleased with her progress and she came home once more. She was very tired and for some time could only droop about the house, lacking energy or enthusiasm for anything. This was an important time at school with first year mock A level exams looming up in May and June.

Not to be outdone, Ros gradually pulled herself back to normal, with a resilience and intent that were quite amazing. Being off school for nearly three months and in pain for a lot of that time had left Ros weakened by her experiences, but now she was ready for some action. She borrowed notes from her friends again, the teachers supported her with extra help and she returned to studying. She started driving lessons, too, and went off once a week with a rather elderly and velour clad driving instructor.

But vWd continued its relentless course. At the end of April, Ros had a very bad nosebleed. Over six days of bleeding, during which she only had one day at school, she gave herself an injection at home. When that did not work she went to Pendlebury for a dose of the old-fashioned cryo. She attended Stockport Infirmary for a nose pack, but bleeding continued, so she went back to Pendlebury and was kept in for 48 hour bed rest. Now seventeen years old, in a children's ward, on a bed that was really too small for her, surrounded by children and crying babies, she was cross and unhappy.

The staff of the haemophilia unit at Pendlebury realised that Ros was too grown-up to be treated there, but felt reluctant to transfer her to the adult haemophilia centre at Manchester Royal Infirmary. Dr Evans arranged for the haematologist at Withington to take over her care and provide supplies of factor VIII for home treatment. This was good – it was nearer home and Ros had been cared for by him and his department while under Prof. Dr Evans would continue the annual review of her health.

We were all very proud of Ros when she passed her driving test first time and when she won first prize in the school music competition, singing a Carpenters' song, *We've only just begun,* with two friends. At the end of year clinic appointment to see Prof, Ros decided that she should see him on her own and I agreed. More and more she was taking on responsibility for her own care.

Work towards A levels and visits to universities and colleges kept Ros busy the following spring. The mock exams came and went and Ros celebrated her eighteenth birthday. She was studying hard, sometimes having study sessions with Kitty, who was also working for A levels. There were days when she felt unwell; while she had no specific symptoms, she needed to rest at home.

Because of pain in her ankle over some years Ros had been referred to an orthopaedic surgeon at Withington Hospital, and an X-ray of her ankle showed that there was a bony lump in it. A scan was done and the consultant told us that this was a cyst in her ankle joint and that there was nothing he could do. This was depressing news. She was in pain after any significant periods of walking or standing.

But Ros, sensibly and in her indomitable way, got on cheerfully with her studies and social activities. As the A levels drew near she took a small part in a play, *Once A Catholic* , a catholic school comedy, with our local Garrick Theatre's youth group. After a member of the cast withdrew she took a much larger part, as a rebellious teenager. As she practised her part the air was blue around the house! She sat for the final exams. Then came the excitement and emotion of leaving school, and the leavers' ball to celebrate this. We hunted for a ball gown and finally hired a lovely dress from a shop in Knutsford. Despite looking so beautiful, she rarely got a date.

Ros was busy all that summer with applications for university or college places. Because of the time she had had off during these two crucial years of study, it was difficult to predict what her A level results might be, though the teachers at Cheadle Hulme were reasonably confident that she would do well. When her results came in we were all pleased with her C, D and E grades, though she failed biology – John's specialist subject. After all she had gone through physically, mentally and emotionally, I thought these were very good results. I was really proud of Ros and hoped very much that she could get a university place.

Now the pressure was on. Ros learned a Shakespeare sonnet for an audition at Stratford-upon-Avon College, but was turned down for a place. A college in west London also auditioned and rejected her. Time was fast moving towards the start of the new academic year. Ros really wanted to study away from home. She had looked forward to doing what most of her friends had already succeeded in doing, getting places at university. She had nearly resigned herself to living at home, or taking a year out and working when, in September, she received an offer from Huddersfield university. We were all thrilled!

Ros had contacted the tutor for the course she wanted – Drama and Media Studies – and he asked how she had done in her A levels.

When Ros replied that she thought she had done rather well, considering that she had had three months in hospital in the first year of sixth form, the tutor was curious to know why. Ros told him about her condition and after further conversation he responded with the offer of a place. A week later we went to Huddersfield, to sort out form filling and registration and try to find a place for Ros to live. It was only a week before term started.

We met the course tutor and after the paperwork was completed he took us to the accommodation office. There was a queue a mile long, and we all duly waited patiently in it. When our turn came, the tutor had a word with the staff and went into the back of the office. After a few minutes consultation he returned with the news that he had booked Ros the last room in halls, normally reserved for overseas students. What a relief! I was so thankful that she would not be in some grotty flat or bedsit in a strange town. It transpired later that the course tutor suffered from arthritis, so was very sympathetic towards Ros.

Now we only had three days to get everything ready for Ros to move. We frantically shopped for pots, pans, cutlery and food, as her accommodation was self-catering. Determined to start when everyone else did, Ros did not want to miss the beginning of term and Freshers' Week. It was a hard slog getting everything done, but we did it.

We drove Ros to Huddersfield for the start of her three-year course. I was feeling anxious for her and her new life style. We had had so little time to get ready that thoughts about her haemophilia care were for once pushed away. However, she had supplies of factor VIII with her and had been demonstrating for some time that she could cope perfectly well with her injections. I knew that Ros was extremely able and sensible and would cope with her difficulties, while it was *me* who might go to pieces.

Going to university was a big step towards independence for Ros, and for us the start of a different kind of worry, mainly fear of the unknown. Ros had once been asked how she coped with her bleeding problem. Her reply was, "I do the injections and look after myself and my Mum does the worrying". I heard this remark and had vowed not to be unnecessarily anxious. However, on that dull, wet evening's drive back from Huddersfield I cried for most of the hour long journey home.

Letter from Paul

Chapter Ten

The orthopaedic surgeon at Withington had said he could not do anything for Ros's ankle. I therefore discussed with Dr Evans the possibility of her being seen at St Thomas's Hospital in London. Some years before at a north west group meeting at Manchester Royal Infirmary we had heard a talk given by two doctors from St Thomas's. We had been impressed by the work they were doing in their joint haemophilia and orthopaedic clinic. Dr Evans agreed to contact them and before long Ros received an appointment for an initial consultation with them. We travelled to London early in February for this appointment and saw both the specialists in their joint clinic. They shared their thoughts on the possibilities of surgery on the ankle and, with their humorous banter, made an impressive team.

A few weeks later Ros phoned to say that they would operate on her ankle. The orthopaedic surgeon would remove the bony cyst and hopefully cure the pain; the haematologist would keep her bleeding problems under control. Keen to have this operation, Ros had to wait some months before it could be done.

A debate ensued about who was to pay for this operation. Ros was living in Huddersfield and had a new GP there, but her permanent address was still in Stockport. Her haemophilia care was under Manchester and she was having the operation in London. I spoke to somebody at the local area health authority in Stockport. We discussed the situation and they assured me that the operation would be paid for. The amusing part was when they said, "but I shouldn't be discussing this with you!" It was unknown for patients or their families to get involved in such matters.

Ros's university grant only covered basic living expenses and other necessities drew heavily on her small budget, be it a train fare home or a new supply of plasters, bandages or sanitary towels. Because her mobility was restricted, she applied for and was eventually awarded, the government disability living allowance (DLA). Soon information came about the motability scheme, whereby all the DLA money awarded to her could be put directly towards owning a vehicle. Ros, needing a car to help her get about, thought this was an excellent scheme and started to look for a suitable vehicle.

Ros was enjoying university life. She had made good friends with the girls in her halls of residence, she was enjoying the lectures and working hard. The first year was soon gone and at the end of the summer term Ros took delivery of her first car under the motability scheme, a neat little red Corsa. It was some time before she could really get used to this new acquisition as, after only three weeks of ownership, she was admitted into St Thomas's for her ankle operation.

St Thomas's Hospital stood on the south bank of the river Thames, opposite the Houses of Parliament. The main entrance to the hospital was more like a modern shopping mall, with shops, restaurants and places to sit. This modern façade gave way to older parts of the building, but much modernisation had been carried out to make the atmosphere welcoming. Standing in Ros's six-bedded ward on the fifth floor, we had splendid views of the river and over London. Ros was to be in hospital for a week. I stayed with an acquaintance near Kew Gardens.

We had arrived at the hospital at 4.15pm on the first day, after waiting at home for a phone call from them to say that there would be a bed available. I was horrified to discover that Ros was due to have her operation the next morning. I could not see how her clotting levels could be raised to safe limits so quickly. I was told not to worry and tried to put my faith in the haematologist's knowledge and skill. Treatment was started at 8.00pm. I spent a restless night at Kew and went back to the hospital at midday the next day. Ros was very pale and still in a post-operative state, but all was well. She had been given a new French vWd factor and overnight her clotting levels had risen to 140%! Although this seemed an alarming increase to me, the vWd factor only had a short life and effect. Very soon Ros's levels were dropping to more normal amounts. She continued on this French product for the rest of her stay and brought some home for follow-up treatment. For the next few days in hospital Ros had variable bleeding times, but they were all within reasonably safe limits.

Four days after her operation Ros was free of drips and drip stands and was mobile on crutches. Her plaster cast was removed and she had some physiotherapy. On our return home we enquired if Ros could continue on this seeming 'wonder' treatment but were told that she could not have it. It was very expensive, always a consideration for hospital budget makers, and it also had a short life and effectiveness. We were reliant on the treatments that Ros was prescribed; there was no cure for vWd or for haemophilia as yet. Each year a little scientific progress was made, but the steps towards a cure were tiny and almost insignificant.

For the next six weeks Ros was fairly immobile. I spent a lot of time ferrying her here and there, playing taxi driver, while she went to the pub to meet her school friends or to hospital to fetch treatment supplies or for doctors' appointments. Kitty often came to keep her company and later her whole family took Ros with them for a two-week holiday in Majorca. This was a great success, as the hotel had a shuttle service, which took guests to the nearest beach. Ros came back with photos of her on crutches in the sea and on the dance floor at the hotel. Early in September Kitty went with her to London for a follow-up appointment. Her ankle was still very painful, but she was gradually walking more and more on it. The specialists were pleased with her progress, but she still had to take care.

Ros (with crutches!)
on holiday in Majorca

By the December visit to St Thomas's Ros was fully mobile, but still having pain in her ankle. The follow-up X-rays showed that the ankle was still arthritic. The two eminent doctors decided that her pain was due more to the arthritis than to the removal of the bony cyst. They suggested that if the pain got worse it would be possible to fuse the bones in the ankle joint, but this would fix it at a right angle. Ros decided that she would prefer to live with the pain and retain a normal joint.

During Ros's stay in St Thomas's a comment was made which, at the time, had little impact on me. Before her operation a doctor had asked her what her hepatitis C status was. Ros did not know what he was talking about. He told her that her notes recorded that she had tested positive for HCV, the hepatitis C virus. This she knew to be bad and she must have told me about it. At the time I was more concerned about her operation and did not have any particular reaction. We were ignorant of the facts and unaware of its true significance. We knew little or nothing about this virus, but as the weeks and months went by we became more alert to the subject. Now that Ros was carrying the virus we were forced to be more informed.

Hepatitis is inflammation of the liver. The common types of hepatitis are caused by viral infections. Hepatitis A and B are known about and there is a vaccine to protect against these, but at the time of writing there is no vaccine for hepatitis C. In 1989 the viral agent for the hepatitis non-A non-B condition had been isolated and named hepatitis C and a screening test for the detection of HCV on blood donations had become available. This test was immediately widely used in Europe and in the USA for ensuring that blood transfusions and blood products to be used for patients were as safe as possible. The UK, however, lagged behind the rest of Europe, although many leading liver specialists were pushing for the National Blood Transfusion Service (NBTS) to use this test. The NBTS rejected the use of this screening process, on the grounds that the test would produce a total of seven false positive cases per UK working day, thus making a lot of extra work and causing unnecessary worry for the donors. They did not change their policy for two years. This meant that for two years HCV infected blood donations were being pooled with other donations to make blood products for patients with haemophilia and other bleeding disorders.

The facts about HCV were documented in the bulletins and leaflets produced by the Haemophilia Society. Most people receiving treatment for haemophilia, vWd and other rarer clotting disorders before 1985 were likely to have been infected with HCV. One of the leaflets produced by the Haemophilia Society used cautious language for categorising the sufferers. For severe haemophiliacs it stated, *will have been infected*, but for the mild to moderate sufferers, those with vWd or carriers it was, *may have been infected or were also at risk.* The transmission of this virus is mainly through blood to blood contact. Other people not suffering from haemophilia had contracted the virus through blood transfusion. Even more people were infected through sharing needles and other equipment while injecting with drugs. There was a possibility that a few people could contract HCV through the use of unsterilised equipment during tattoo or skin piercing procedures or through any work in the medical field when accidental needlestick injury had occurred.

The symptoms of HCV are wide ranging. Some people have no symptoms at all, while others experience quite a number, the most common being a feeling of general fatigue. Jaundice, nausea, loss of appetite, depression and lack of concentration can also occur. The hepatitis C virus causes the liver to become inflamed and, if this happens over a long period, can cause the liver cells to die, leaving scar tissue in their place. This damage, known as fibrosis, causes the liver to become very badly scarred and can develop into cirrhosis. Some people with cirrhosis will go on to develop liver cancer. At this stage the only option is to hope for a liver transplant.

Hepatitis C now became our major concern. Bleeding was a minor issue compared to this new cruel virus, which had already caused deaths among the haemophilia population. Following Ros's abrupt learning that she was hepatitis C positive, the truth of this virus began to penetrate our minds, slowly at first but with increasing impact as we learned more about it. We were puzzled as to why Ros had not been told by the staff at her own haemophilia centre. Was it because they were scared of their patients' reactions? How had this contamination occurred?

Like a slow bleed, the knowledge of this deadly virus was trickling through the haemophilia community, through the centres, the society, the patients and their families. Those old feelings of isolation that I had felt when Ros was small returned, along with a feeling of helplessness; helplessness against something much more powerful than we could imagine, a cruel and as yet, incurable virus. Why was this happening to us?

As we heard more about hepatitis C, read articles and books and talked to other sufferers, the anger came – anger at why this should afflict Ros, just when her life was opening up before her, when she was looking forward to the working world and full independence. From what we began to learn of hepatitis C we knew that the virus could stay quietly in the bloodstream for ten or twenty years before making itself felt. Had she been suffering from this virus for most of her life? Did this new virus explain all those days when she just did not feel quite well? Worry and anxiety had been part of our lives until Ros was able to cope on her own. Now they returned, with a deep concern about the future, and mainly with the question, would this kill her?

We were amazed to discover that some people with haemophilia were having transplants. It was very dangerous for anyone with a bleeding disorder to have major surgery. Amazingly, those haemophiliacs who were ill, and brave enough to undergo transplant, would be cured of haemophilia, since clotting factor VIII is made in the liver and their new liver would produce it. When statistics on transplants became available, 80% of patients were still alive three years after their transplant. Unfortunately, the patients would have to take immunosuppressant drugs for the rest of their lives; also the HCV virus would remain in the bloodstream and eventually attack the new liver.

The future for Ros, for us and for most of the haemophilia population, began to look very bleak. Ros dying from a major bleed had always been a possibility but one I had never had to face, due to the good care that she received in the hospitals. Now it looked as if all those years of work and care to keep Ros as normal and healthy as possible would be undone by a virus that could kill, yet had been transmitted through life-saving treatment. What was going on? Why was Ros, who had suffered enough from bleeds, being put to this new test? There were no answers.

The impact of hepatitis C began to hit home.

Excerpt from Ros's submission to the Archer Inquiry in 2007

I found out that I had contracted hepatitis C from contaminated blood products inadvertently.

When I was 19 I was sent to St Thomas's Hospital in London for an operation on my ankle. While I was being prepped for the operation the consultant, I think it was Dr Savidge, asked me about my having hepatitis C. I did not know what he was talking about. I had no idea at that time that I had contracted hepatitis C. It was obviously in my notes but none of my doctors in Manchester had ever mentioned it to me. This was how the news was broken. I was sitting on the ward, surrounded by nurses doing their job and other patients – I felt frozen in time. Dr Savidge may have tried to explain more seeing my shock but I don't remember anything else he said.

I never confronted my own specialists as to why I had not been told I had contracted this life threatening virus. When I asked for more information on my return home, I was not told about the effect hepatitis C could have and the prospects for liver damage, cirrhosis and liver cancer. I was only told that it was a virus that could take in excess of 20 years to cause any problems – irrespective of the fact that I could have contracted this anytime after my first injection 19 years ago, a fact I was unaware of at the time. I was advised that I should be careful not to drink too much. Not advised to avoid alcohol, only to drink a bit less with no real guidance as to how much was a bit. I was not told anything about the risk to sexual partners; luckily I had none at that time.....

Chapter Eleven

The impact of the AIDS virus in the 1980's on haemophiliacs was devastating. A support group and trust fund, the Macfarlane Trust, had been set up, following the successful fight for compensation for those who had suffered or died from HIV. Now a new group of victims within the Haemophilia Society, embittered and angry about acquiring HCV, formed a pressure group to work towards getting compensation. Some people were co-infected with HIV and HCV.

Because of our involvement with the Haemophilia Society, both locally and nationally, we were able to attend a meeting of this new pressure group, the Manor House group, at the chairman's conference and AGM at Coventry. I found it a rather depressing occasion and did not feel drawn to join in. Despite this, we soon became involved with the Manor House group, and attended many meetings on Sundays at Barlaston, near Stoke-on-Trent. The house where the meetings were held, a former home to one of the Wedgewood family and now a hotel, stands in its own grounds on the edge of the village, looking out over the adjacent countryside. A calming atmosphere pervades this place, where the group has experienced much heart-searching, anger, frustration and sadness. A tree has been planted in the grounds and a plaque placed beside it, in memory of those who have died of HCV.

Attending other Haemophilia Society national meetings and conferences, we heard several speakers on HCV and twice heard a consultant hepatologist from Queen Elizabeth's Hospital in Birmingham. Little did we know, but it would not be long before Ros came under this consultant's care. Our copious notes from the conferences recorded the up-to-date views on diagnosis, treatment and attitudes generally to HCV, about which much was still unknown. The current practice was that haematologists would diagnose haemophiliacs through regular checks for antibodies to HCV and by performing liver function tests. These could not give as clear a picture of the state of the liver as a biopsy, but they were the safest option for bleeders. It was apparent at these early meetings that most hepatologists were clearly unhappy about doing a biopsy on a patient with haemophilia, because of patient safety, the inconvenience to the patient and the expense of the blood products needed to cover the procedure. The only available treatment for HCV at this time was interferon.

The possibility of compensation for haemophiliacs affected by HCV was being considered by the department of health, after much lobbying from the Haemophilia Society and the Manor House group. The media occasionally printed articles and letters from haemophiliacs who were angry at the lack of awareness of their situation. Television programmes were made, covering the subject of HCV and the safety of blood products. Ironically, the 1996 ITV *World in Action* programme on HCV was shown on the same day as the parliamentary under secretary of state, John Horam, announced that there would be no compensation paid out to haemophiliacs who had contracted the HCV virus. He believed that to make an across-the-board payment, or to set up a hardship fund, would be inappropriate use of government funds. After this depressing announcement we were sorry not to be able to join a demonstration and lobby of parliament, because of work commitments. Later, if a demonstration was organised, I took a day of unpaid leave from my work, in order to add strength to our cause. I started to keep a file of press cuttings, reports, articles and letters, on the subject of HCV and our fight for compensation.

Through my work I had kept abreast of the current adoption scene. Something now came to our attention, which made both John and I particularly incensed. It was a recent proposal by John Major and the government for charging prospective adopters. This little paragraph included in *The Adoption Review, Part VIII* of the *Adoption Law Review* read, in part, *We recommend that legislation should make provision for local authorities and approved adoption societies to charge for some services according to means.* It went on to describe, in very woolly terms, where some of these charges might be laid. This proposal had been leaked to the media in July 1993 and the *Guardian* newspaper ran an article. We wrote to the paper describing the financial burden already imposed on us since adopting our children, for example, repairs to our house and property after abnormal wear and tear, running a car to get to the hospital, extra washing of stained clothes and bedding and so on. We ended our letter, *Adoption certainly saves money. What would happen if all these (adopted) children remained in the care of the local authority? This government seems to have lost sight of reality.* A friend, who worked for the *Guardian,* faxed our letter. It was printed in a prime position on the letters page the next day, to our great satisfaction. Two days later the government announced a U-turn on adoption charging. We really felt that we had changed the world overnight! The PPIAS newsletter recorded in August that *the proposal that prospective adopters should be charged for assessment met with such universal condemnation that the planned publication of the White Paper had been delayed.*

I now decided to go back to full-time work with children; it was where my skills lay. I had enjoyed being in touch with all aspects of adoption, but I was not enjoying office based work in central Manchester. I had heard rumours that Paul's former educational psychologist had left the education department in Stockport to set up a school for autistic children. I was very interested to hear of the work he was doing and wanted to be a part of it. The school was newly opened and was run under the auspices of a local charity in south Manchester. It was situated in a leafy suburb of Stockport, in very pleasant grounds and with open fields nearby. My only experience of autistic children had been at Charnwood, many years before, but I thought I had something to offer. After a successful interview I started work there as an educational assistant.

Meanwhile, I had volunteered to be on the Parent Support Network, set up by the family worker at the Haemophilia Society. There were a dozen or so volunteers scattered around the UK, ready to take calls from families with difficulties or concerns. I had received a number of calls from families with vWd and all were anxious for more information about this disorder. I found responding to these families very interesting and realised just how much I knew about vWd from living with Ros all these years. With the help of the Haemophilia Society, a network of families with vWd slowly developed. The contacts lapsed over the years, but one thing emerged – women and girls who were bleeders were beginning to be given a higher profile.

Ros had reached her final year at university, gathering new friends around her and keeping in touch with the old ones. Many of these

Ros at her 21st birthday party

friends joined our extended family to celebrate her 21st birthday over a weekend in March. On the evening of the party, Ros looked stunning in a dark green velvet dress. It was a gratifying experience to see this lovely young lady, my daughter, looking so well and happy. When I thought of all the pain and suffering she had gone through in her young life, I was grateful for all the good things that had happened to her as well. How I wished she could find happiness with a loving and supportive partner.

During her final exams Ros had a setback with a very bad bleed. John and I were having a few days' holiday in the Lake District. Ros phoned us at our guest-house one morning upset and tearful. She had really bad stomach cramps and was losing a lot of blood. We were as consoling as we could be from a distance and encouraged her to go to the hospital in Huddersfield. I was worried enough to leave details of our planned day out with the guest-house owners. How I thought they could contact us I do not know. We were *still* without mobile phones. Mid-afternoon we were in Eskdale eating ice creams and phoned Ros from a public telephone. She was not feeling so bad, but the hospital had been unable to treat her. The hospital in Huddersfield was classed as an associate haemophilia centre, which meant that it did not have the same level of service as the comprehensive care haemophilia centres and did not have stocks of clotting factor treatment. They suggested that she should go to Manchester Royal Infirmary (MRI), which was her main centre of treatment now, having transferred her care to them after being under Withington Hospital. This she managed to do next day, driving slowly and carefully down the M62, stopping at every service station to go to the loo. The doctors took her blood count and it was low. She had treatment there and returned to Huddersfield. Two days later we fetched her home. She was white and shaky, and as her blood count was getting lower all the time she was given a blood transfusion at MRI. That same evening we all drove back to Huddersfield. She soon perked up and finished revising for her final exams. When finals were over she enjoyed parties with her friends before coming home to look for a job.

After university Ros did something she had always wanted to do. She spent five weeks in Chile. She was thrilled at the prospect of travelling to South America. I was not. Many worries assailed me, but I tried to keep them to myself. Ros had been away from home now for three years and I knew she was coping very well. Home treatment was such a relief. Ros had travelled abroad to Germany with us and with school and had been away to Majorca with Daniel and Veronica, Kitty and Karen, but the other side of the world seemed to me quite another matter. The greatest consolation for me lay in the fact that Ros would stay with Kitty and her grandparents, in their home in Santiago. As part of her Spanish course at the University of Liverpool, Kitty was just finishing a year of study in Chile, finalising her dissertation on los Retornados (the returned ones), those citizens of Chile, banished by Pinochet, who had had the bravery to return to their homeland.

Ros booked a flight from Manchester on the shuttle service to Heathrow, ready for the long haul flight to Santiago. She had a suitcase full of treatment with her, a covering letter for the customs and her insurance. John and I went to see her off and we were all quietly aware of the significance of her journey. As she was about to go through the departures gate, I gave her an enormous hug and said, "You know I love you very much", to which she gave a similar reply. Not wanting to frighten her when she already had to face a sixteen hour flight alone, I suppressed the ominous thoughts which were in my mind. We parted with a smile and a wave. The next evening the phone rang. It was Ros phoning from Santiago. She had arrived safely and all was well. My diary entry for that day says ... *she and Kitty, giggling, several thousand miles away!* I was vastly reassured. From then on, until she came safely home again, I did not know where she was or what she was doing and this enabled me to blank out the worry.

Before she left for Chile, Ros had been interviewed for a job as a sales assistant at the nearby new John Lewis store at Cheadle, Stockport, which was due to open in September. While she was away, two things occurred which I needed to tell her. The first was her friend Abi, phoning from Huddersfield with Ros's degree results – she achieved a 2:1. I phoned Ros with this good news. We were thrilled that she had graduated so successfully. The second was the offer of a job at John Lewis. When this letter came, I knew that Ros and Kitty would be backpacking somewhere in the north of Chile. Ros had arranged to ring me while they were out of Santiago, to find out if there was any news. This she did, from Iquique. I then wrote to John Lewis, telling them where she was and accepting the job on her behalf.

Postcard sent from Ros in Chile

This five-day backpacking trip took the girls up through the Atacama Desert and briefly over the border into Peru. Both of them were adventurous. Ros had already given herself more than one injection, and it must have been a nuisance carrying the extra luggage of supplies. The high altitude of the desert may have caused the bad nosebleed that she suffered on the way back down the cross-country route to Santiago. They had arrived at San Pedro, a remote little town, by bus in the early evening and there was a rush to get accommodation. There were large numbers of other backpackers, owing to an annual festival soon to take place nearby. San Pedro had very basic amenities, dirt streets, adobe (sun dried brick) housing and electricity for only two hours each morning and evening. It was important that Kitty and Ros found somewhere quickly, particularly as Ros needed to do an injection. Her ankle was hurting as well, as they had walked a lot during the day. Everyone ran off the bus; every time Kitty and Ros reached a guest-house or B and B all available accommodation was already gone. At one place they found a twin room, but it was quite expensive and had outside shower facilities, so they turned it down and carried on looking. After a further half an hour dragging their suitcases around the village, with no luck and a dog that kindly watered Ros's bag, they decided to take the original room. However, on returning there the owners apologetically explained that it had been taken. The girls were starting to worry but the family offered to move out of their bedroom and sleep in the kitchen so that Kitty and Ros could have a bed. They ended up sharing the room with another desperate couple, the room separated by a blanket as a makeshift screen. Kitty having explained the situation as best she could, Ros was finally able to do her injection in the kitchen, watched by three generations of the family who owned the house. And eventually the nosebleed stopped.

Kitty felt that Ros was annoyed with her condition on this occasion, not cross with herself but upset and frustrated. She and Kitty were doing what thousands of young people do every year, picking up a guide book, packing a rucksack and going out and having adventures, seeing the world. Ros had very much wanted to do this, so her anger and frustration over this incident were perfectly understandable.

The new John Lewis store duly opened and after the holiday Ros started her job as a sales assistant. After a few months she began to feel very tired from all the standing, as there was no seating at the tills and she was working ten-hour shifts. One evening she came in crying from the pain in her ankle. Despite this, she continued in the job for a year and really enjoyed the work. I was concerned that her ankles would be seriously damaged by all the standing and she, too, was finding it difficult to do the job while in pain.

The following autumn she found a new sedentary job in the box office of the Bridgewater Hall, the new concert hall in Manchester. This only lasted a short time as one of the managers from John Lewis, with whom she was still in touch, offered her a job as social secretary back at the store. Ros went into this role with very little experience but lots of enthusiasm, following another equally successful interview. She moved into a house in Didsbury, south Manchester, with four other young professional people. I was pleased that she could continue her independence by living away from home.

Early in the following new year, Ros phoned one day to say that she had had discussions over her health with the haemophilia centre director at MRI. She had decided to start the interferon treatment for HCV. The haematologist had been doing regular liver function tests on Ros's blood, and he had recommended treatment. These blood tests are used frequently and are the preferred method of assessing the state of the liver for most people with haemophilia. There is an enzyme present in the liver, alanine aminotransferase. High levels of this enzyme in a blood sample may indicate liver cell damage. Ros's levels had been found to be elevated, so treatment had been discussed. It was later discovered that her test results could have been affected by the high doses of hormone pills that she was taking to control her periods.

Most haematologists were reluctant to recommend liver biopsy, which would give a more accurate picture of the state of the patient's liver, because of the risks involved with bleeding from the site of the insertion of the biopsy needle. They continued their care of HCV patients and did not refer them to liver specialists.

A few weeks later I went with Ros for the initial consultation and the start of the treatment. She was to be given the first injection by the haemophilia nurse and then continue the injections herself at home. We had a long consultation with the doctor first, in which the questions and worries we both had were discussed thoroughly. Then the nurse talked Ros through how to do the injection. The interferon was to be administered into the thigh, abdomen or any fatty tissue, three times a week for the next three months and possibly for a whole year. We knew about the side effects of interferon from hearing the speakers on HCV and from articles we had read, and these side effects could be quite severe. Those embarking on this treatment could expect to feel lousy for the first 24 to 48 hours after the injection, suffering symptoms similar to bad 'flu. They could expect depression, mild or severe. In some cases this depression could lead to feelings of suicide. Paracetemol was recommended to patients taking interferon, to help to ease the pain and flu like symptoms.

I was shocked and horrified, at the end of the consultation, to find Ros being handed a prescription and told to go to the pharmacy for supplies. This virus had been given to Ros through her blood products; in my opinion the very least the health service could do would be to pay for her treatment. Ros had run up some debt while at university and had taken out student loans to help her. She had only been working for eighteen months and was starting to live independently. She was not in a position to afford regular prescriptions for possibly a whole year. The use of a pre-payment certificate only slightly reduced the cost.

I phoned Ros the day after this first treatment. She had had a very rough night, but was resting at home. As usual she said she was all right. The first few weeks of interferon injections were horrible for her, as she settled into a routine, feeling groggy and depressed. She slept a great deal, taking paracetemol to ease the aches, getting out of bed around lunchtime most days. The side effects were dreadful. Ros felt as if her bones were rotting. Some days she felt constant pressure on her shoulders, as though someone was sitting on them, weighing her down. On other days her headaches were so bad that she felt her head might explode. The injections themselves into stomach or thigh, left bruises and tiny pinprick holes, which often bled for some hours. Ros was still a bleeder after all. I was frightened one day, when I came out of work and saw Ros's car in the car park. We always arranged to meet, but there she was, unannounced, so I knew her spirits must be very low. We went to the local Marks and Spencer cafe, where I tried to cheer her up over a cup of tea, but I do not know if I was much use. I felt so bad, because she felt so ill. I was suffering with her, but had no idea how it felt. We both just sat and stared at each other, wallowing in the misery of it all.

Ros tried hard to keep hold of her job. She injected the interferon on a Friday evening, so the weekend would be rough, but she would hope to work on a Monday before the next injection. She tried to work on Wednesdays and Fridays too before the evening injections laid her low once more. At the end of the first month of treatment her liver function test results showed that her HCV status was much the same. I worried constantly about her and felt quite depressed at her condition. She struggled on with her job, but found that she could give less and less to it as the months went by. She could not concentrate for long, so trying to organise a plethora of social activities for the store staff was extremely taxing. She would sit at her desk trying not to fall asleep. In spite of her best efforts she accepted that she could not continue working whilst on the treatment.

Her friends at this time were most supportive and sent cards and letters and phoned up with cheery greetings. Ros had further liver function tests and the results suggested that it would be desirable to continue the interferon injections for the next nine months. Although initially very supportive of her decision to stop working, John Lewis decided they could not keep her job open after this news. They ended her contract in September.

Ros was not going to be beaten. Having no work, feeling ill all the time, she began to take an interest in the campaign for justice for people with HCV. This campaign had been building up over the past few years, since the rejection by the department of health over the issue of compensation. Ros felt this was something she could focus on – other than how crap she was feeling.

21st birthday letter of thanks

35 Crescent Park
Heaton Norris
STOCKPORT
SK4 2HT

10 April 1995

Dear   Mum + Dad

Firstly I want to apologise for this impersonal and lazy way of writing, I'd much rather write to everyone in person but I'm sure you understand that it would take me an extremely long time.

I am really writing to thank you for coming to my birthday party and to thank you for any cards and gifts you gave me. I did very well for presents and got far more than was necessary, although of course they are all greatly appreciated. If you donated to the "Chile Fund" you will be pleased to hear that I will be booking my flight in the next couple of weeks. The plan at the moment is to go from 24 June until 31 July which will allow me five weeks to experience the country and culture.

I had a splendid time at my party and, as you probably noticed, had far too many drinks bought for me. I hope that you enjoyed the evening as much as I. I realised that sort of thing was not going to appeal to everyone but really it was just a good excuse to see people I've not seen for ages and reunite friends. It was wonderful to be with so many lovely people and realise how lucky I am to have such skill relations and friends.

Thank you again for making my 21st birthday one I shall remember until I'm at least 22, when I may be tempted to have another b'day bash (although I haven't told mum that yet and I probably wouldn't survive if I tried!) Also sorry again for this computorised effort but I've got to practise because in the next five weeks I must produce two dissertations, three essays, a portfolio and a report! And of course 40 thank you letters!

Do stay in touch and keep me up to date with how you are. Hope to see you again soon.

lots of love

Rosamunde
xx

Chapter Twelve

In the 1960's, I had joined the Campaign for Nuclear Disarmament (CND) and had marched from Aldermaston to London carrying a banner. I had stood quietly on Quaker vigils for peace from time to time. However, I had never put any energy into serious lobbying or campaigning. Now we began to support Ros in the protest against the government's decision on compensation

The government was now taking a very different line to the one they had taken on the HIV infection among haemophiliacs. They maintained that HCV was nowhere near as serious as HIV, there was no stigma attached to sufferers and a cure was possible. We knew different. We knew that people with haemophilia were dying of HCV related illnesses. Some were surviving after liver transplants, but the virus would remain in the blood stream and attack the new liver. We knew about stigma, too. Within the Manor House group one sufferer had neighbours who would not speak to him, because of his infection with HCV. Another family with a ten-year old son invited ten of his friends for a birthday party; only three accepted and two of these had been instructed not to eat the food at the house. Ros, too, found that new relationships did not last. She was, by nature, a very honest person and could not lie about her condition and its further complications. If she did go out on a date, work was often a common topic of conversation. As she was not working because of her treatment, she would explain about her health. Often the relationship went no further.

Effective treatments for HCV were still being developed. At this time around 20% of patients on interferon would be in remission at the end of their treatment. As we were seeing with Ros, the side effects were most unpleasant. It was known that approximately 30% of people having it would have to be taken off it as these effects were impossible to live with. The effectiveness of treatment depended on the strain of HCV. Those with the HCV strain known as genotype 1, had a low response rate to treatment (20-30%). Those with the strains known as genotypes 2 and 3 had a much higher response rate (70%). Ros had 'luckily' contracted genotype 2.

The new Blood Products Laboratory had been slow to develop in the 70's. The government had imported blood donations from paid donors in the USA, many of whom were prisoners and drug addicts. From these donations the virus had been transmitted into UK blood products, and was a cause of the outcry now. It was not a pretty scenario. A letter from Stanford University Medical Center to the Blood Products Laboratory in Elstree, dated 1975, warned of the dangers. It stated, *One commercial product for Factor deficiency has proved extraordinarily hazardous, a 50 – 90 percent rate of icteric hepatitis developing from it. About half of these can prove fatal. This source of blood is 100 percent from Skid – Row derelicts ... Half, if not more of the cases of posttransfusion hepatitis are caused by an agent other than Hepatitis A or B. Whatever this other agent(s) may be, it still seems to be more frequently encountered in the lower socio-economic groups of paid and prison donors. It is minimal among voluntary donors.* It was some years later that we saw a copy of this letter.

We wrote to our MP, Ann Coffey, in the autumn of 1997, asking her to support us in putting pressure on the then secretary of state for health, Frank Dobson, who was reviewing the situation. He had held a meeting with delegates from the Haemophilia Society and was looking at how HCV had affected those suffering and their families. We thought that he would make an early announcement, possibly reversing the policy of the previous Conservative administration. Our hopes were raised; we clung on to this news, listening to news bulletins and watching TV for any sign of this. Over the next few months no announcement came. By the following February, we wrote again to our MP, telling her of the stress that we felt in not hearing; again we heard nothing. We started a regular correspondence with our MP and with the department of health which was to continue for many years. The replies from the department of health were not very forthcoming. When they did deign to reply, we found their comments evasive and irrelevant. When pressed for answers to our questions or comments they would reply with the same standard sentences, the paragraphs ordered differently, like students copying each other's work.

Members of the Manor House group planned to hold a second

demonstration outside parliament and then to go inside and lobby our MPs; we wanted to join this. All of us felt hurt and angry at the way we had been treated so far, having our hopes raised and then dashed again. We had plenty to be angry and concerned about; all the members of the Manor House had stories to tell about how HCV affected their lives. The Haemophilia Society, too, was also campaigning strongly. The campaign had three goals:

- compensation for the victims of HCV
- a Public Inquiry into the HCV scandal
- supplies of recombinant factor VIII for all.

Recombinant factor VIII was a new genetically engineered product, hopefully free of all viruses. Despite its cost it was made available to all children under 16 years and to new patients in February 1998. Our campaign wanted all people with haemophilia to have access to this product. As a family we were concerned for people we knew. This recombinant factor VIII was not helpful for Ros as the levels of vWd factor were too low.

Ros threw herself into the thick of all the plans for the demonstration and lobby. She had decided she had nothing to lose by going public. She was invited to go to London and join a delegation of Haemophilia Society members and supportive MPs going to Downing Street. The demonstration and lobby by the Manor House was to coincide with this, in July 1998, before parliament closed for the summer recess.

The morning of the demonstration came; we were up at 5.00am. John and I ordered a taxi to take us to MRI, where we caught the coach. Our West Indian taxi driver sang *We shall overcome* to a quiet background of pop music on his car radio. We thought this was a good omen. We met Ros's friend, Louise, one of her house mates and now a good friend, who was coming with us and climbed aboard the coach for London. To combat her tiredness and other symptoms, Ros had travelled the day before, so that she could rest overnight and gather strength for the day. Travelling with other members of the Manor House group produced an energy among us, a fighting spirit in defence of our loved ones. Arriving in London at around 12.30, we walked with our banners and placards through the streets towards parliament. Our bright yellow T-shirts caught people's attention.

Outside parliament we met up with Ros and the delegation which had been to Downing Street and presented a 5000 name petition. They had laid ninety white lilies on the steps of number 10, each lily representing one of the people with haemophilia who had died from HCV so far.

Two or three of the Manor House members chained themselves to the railings outside parliament; one was in a wheelchair. They were soon persuaded, rather amicably by the police, to undo themselves. The police presence was fairly relaxed about us and seemed sympathetic. We gained entrance to the lobby of the House of Commons, where many members were able to reiterate their case with their MPs. At one point we were addressed, briefly, by Lord Alf Morris, which cheered and encouraged us. As a member of the House of Lords and patron, later president, of the Haemophilia Society, he has campaigned tirelessly on our behalf. The day was long and exhausting; we were back home at midnight. We were reported in the press and had TV coverage in some regions.

Following all this excitement we heard that Frank Dobson was expected to make an early announcement, but we had been taken in before by this possibility. Nonetheless, our hopes were raised once more. John and I went off to Switzerland for a holiday, feeling very positive that at last some offer from the government might be forthcoming. We phoned Ros from our hotel to hear that Frank Dobson had made his decision, which was that, *after lengthy and very careful consideration, we have concluded that haemophiliacs who have been infected with HCV through NHS treatment should not receive special payments. Government policy is that compensation or other financial help to particular patients or groups of patients is paid out only where the NHS or individuals working in it have been at fault. The needs of people whose condition results from inadvertent harm is met from benefits available to the population in general (Hansard 28th July 1998).* Anger and disappointment made us determined not to give up. We were even more determined when we saw in the press that six young adults who were at risk of developing Creutzfeld Jacob Disease (CJD) were expecting £1.5 million between them in compensation from the government. This was given because of the psychological trauma of not knowing if they would develop CJD or not, after being given human growth hormone treatment as children. This news gave us further cause to continue our fight for justice.

Ros had been flat hunting and had moved into a Victorian first floor flat in south Manchester, sharing with Louise. A producer from the BBC contacted us; he was interested in doing a programme on HCV and the campaign as part of the *Close Up North* series in the north west region. In August this producer met Ros and me at her flat. After an hour long talk with him we both agreed to take part in this programme and a date for filming was booked a few days later.

Early in September we spent an afternoon with the producer and his cameraman. I had tried hard to prepare myself for this filming session but when the time came I felt tongue-tied and apprehensive. When I did speak I wandered off the point straight away and rambled on rather too long. I had expected more encouragement or direction from the producer but he seemed to expect us just to talk. Ros was brilliant; even though still on the treatment and feeling so dreadful she expressed her thoughts and emotions very well. Later she was filmed with two friends, Louise and Vanessa, walking through Manchester and talking about HCV. She described clearly her longing for a steady relationship, saying, "I thought of putting a singles ad in – 'young, attractive, 24 year old, contaminated, good sense of humour' – who would want that?" The reality she was facing and had not yet come to terms with was the possibility that she might die. She spoke about this so openly. "The other day I found myself thinking about what music I would like for my funeral", she said.

This filming was not all doom and gloom, however. The producer wanted to film Ros giving herself the interferon injection before going to bed. He would return the next morning and film her waking up and reacting to it, a 'before and after' scene. But it was only 6.30pm; Ros had to pull the curtains, climb into bed and do the injection. At the end of this slot she had to switch off her bedside light at the same time that the cameraman switched off his camera light. This was not easy to synchronise; the cameraman hated the sight of needles and was feeling faint! I was sitting in the next room and suddenly peals of laughter could be heard from Ros's bedroom as they failed to hit the light switches at the same time. By the sixth 'take' they got it right!

117

Ros continued to do press and media interviews. Articles featuring her appeared in various newspapers in the Yorkshire and Manchester areas, along with stories from other haemophilia sufferers and their families. She went with other members of the Manor House to Blackpool, to hand out leaflets at the Party conferences. In the middle of October, a few nights before the TV programme was due out, she saw herself in a preview. We watched the programme together and thought the producer had done a good job.

It was heartening to receive phone calls, letters and cards from friends who had seen the programme. *"I do admire the way you both cope"*, wrote one friend. *"It's hard for us to realise the devastating effects it (HCV) has had, but I'm sure the programme will have helped to increase public awareness"*. Another friend wrote, *"We were moved and impressed by how well and how clearly you were able to speak. Maybe it will help achieve some justice for Ros and the rest"*. A long-standing friend, whom I rarely see, was also moved to write. *"I have always been full of admiration for the way in which you all handled the original medical problems"*, she said, *"and although shocked by the situation now I am simply amazed by your strength in this difficult situation"*. Many others wrote with their support and love. Some felt shocked enough to write to their own MPs.

Meanwhile, Ros was quite determined to keep busy to try to take her mind off her situation. She still felt very ill and being out of work and claiming benefits was very miserable for her. She auditioned for, and was given a place in, the prestigious Halle choir. She had always liked singing since her days in the Maia choir in Stockport. It got her out of the house one evening a week, when she had the energy to go. She enrolled at the local college and studied GCSE Spanish and desktop publishing part-time to keep her mind occupied. She helped out as secretary to the Manor House group when she could. I was so proud of the way she kept herself busy and positive; it would have been so easy just to stay in bed all day. On Christmas Day she invited us to the flat and amazingly produced a delicious Christmas dinner.

The long year went by with the interferon injections three times a week. Ros remained far from well and had many days when she needed me to take her to a hospital appointment or bring her some shopping. I supported her as best I could, between my other

Christmas Dinner, cooked by Ros

commitments and my now part-time job at school. Louise left the flat to go travelling and Ros looked for cheaper accommodation. We went flat hunting together in the spring and eventually found a flat quite close to us. Ros was upset by some of the letting agents she spoke to, who were very rude about people claiming benefits.

The treatment ended at last. The blood test results were initially not good, but Ros was advised that further tests in a few months might be different. She still felt ill when three months later further tests showed that she still carried the virus. This was sad news for all of us. All the stresses and strains of the year, losing her job, feeling permanently ill, seemed to have been in vain. What more could life throw at her?

Wednesday, July 22, 1998

Sufferers need justice

A GROUP of MPs and sufferers of a rare blood disease was today laying 90 white lilies on Tony Blair's doorstep at No 10, in a dramatic protest. Each bloom represents the death of a victim of haemophilia, infected by life-threatening hepatitis C through NHS-supplied blood.

More than 4,000 people were affected before action was taken to treat the blood in 1985, to avoid the risk. Among today's deputation was the Wythenshawe and Sale East Labour MP, Paul Goggins, accompanied by haemophiliacs from the city who are facing a bleak life because of the infection. They were joining more than 100 people with haemophilia in a mass lobby of parliament.

Mr Goggins says that these victims are similar to those infected with HIV by contaminated blood: "The only difference is that those with HIV have been offered financial recompense. Those infected with hepatitis C have received nothing. Hepatitis C has destroyed people's lives and shattered families. There might not be a legal case for the Department of Health to answer, but I and many others in parliament feel there is a moral case."

Those haemophiliacs infected with HIV through NHS treatment benefit from a multi-million pound fund, the Macfarlane Trust, set up by the last government. It is bad enough that sufferers of one disease should acquire another during NHS treatment in hospital. But it is manifestly unjust that one group of sufferers with HIV are compensated, yet another get not a penny. Mr Blair should act immediately to end this injustice. These sufferers have had enough of excuses.

Ros the battler rallies round to shake up No 10

STORY: PATRICIA ROBERTS
PICTURE: GARY ROBERTS

LIFE has not been kind to Ros Batten. She learned to cope with a rare bleeding condition she was born with.

But then came the cruel blow that her treatment had been infected with the potentially fatal liver disease hepatitis C.

Three times a week Ros, 24, from Didsbury, who has had to give up her job and lives on £57 a week in benefits, must inject herself with the powerful drug interferon in an attempt to halt the condition.

But the treatment, which she must undergo for a year, has severe side-effects, leaving her utterly drained and exhausted, and there is only a 25 per cent chance that it will be successful.

Today Ros, who has von Willebrand's disease, a condition similar to haemophilia, put off the treatment to muster the energy to join a delegation to 10 Downing Street. The group was delivering a 5,000-name petition begging for government help for similar sufferers.

Ros is among thousands of NHS patients who have been made ill by infected blood supplies. The campaign is spearheaded by the Haemophilia Society. Ninety white lilies were also being laid on the steps of Number 10 — one for each of those who have died from hepatitis C contracted through their treatment.

The society is urging Prime Minister Tony Blair to accept that the government has a moral responsibility to provide financial compensation as it did for those who contracted HIV through infected blood products.

Last September it met Health Secretary Frank Dobson who, it says, promised "a swift response." Ten months on, they are still waiting.

Karin Pappenheim, chief executive of the society, said: "The delay is unacceptable. This government has powerfully stated its commitment to the vulnerable in our society.

"How can they then ignore the plight of this highly vulnerable small group."

Ros, who had dreamed of travelling the world, marrying and having a family, is struggling to keep her independence. She says hepatitis C has affected her whole life and put a strain on her family, especially her mum.

"I can't think about the future and have to live one day at a time.

"I just want someone to accept responsibility for what has happened to people like me."

■ **Comment: Page 8**

■ Ros Batten ... 'I can't think about the future'

Chapter Thirteen

What life *did* throw at Ros was something positive at last.

John, Ros and I went to a haemophilia day in Leeds. During the day Ros said, "We won't be late back, will we? I've got a friend coming". Ros always referred to her friends by name, so I was curious. Raising my eyebrows I turned to her and asked, "A friend? Who, what? Is it a man?" "It might be," replied Ros and I could get nothing more out of her. I was very intrigued and excited for her, though at the back of my mind I was a little apprehensive. What if she was rejected again?

A few days went by. My diary entry records that then 'we had a big chat about the new man in her life'. Ros had been to the wedding of her university friend, Abi, over the course of a weekend in Worcestershire. Her new man, Adrian, was a friend of Abi's brother and that weekend they had met in the local pub. I was thrilled that something positive was happening in Ros's life.

Although things were looking up in Ros's love life and the treatment was over, she was still unable to work and was struggling financially. She could not afford to stay in her flat and she suggested that she might come and live at home again. While we were debating how to fit all her furniture into our already full house, some friends nearby in Cheadle offered her a room and storage space for her furniture in their garage. This was ideal; Ros would be with people of her own age and could maintain her independence. She needed time to think about what she might do next. Ros was determined to look ahead, despite the trauma of the interferon and its awful side effects, the loss of self esteem due to not working and financial hardships. She now had Adrian to talk to, though she was careful to tell him of her problems in very small doses, so that he would not be frightened off.

As she had no career to return to, Ros decided to take a course in computing, hoping that this might lead to a less physically demanding, yet financially rewarding, job that she could possibly do from home. She managed to secure a career development loan and did a six week intensive Oracle database programming course. At the end of the training the college tried to find unpaid placements for the students with a view to them being offered permanent positions. They found Ros a placement with a firm in Chester. This would have been ideal, but over Christmas she and Adrian had decided to move into a rented house in Worcestershire near Adrian's family farm. After discussing her situation with the new company, they offered Ros a paid position immediately. Ros began the new year by staying in Chester during the week and travelling home to Worcestershire at weekends.

Travelling to and fro took up much of her energy; she was still recovering from the interferon and was having intermittent bleeding problems. I admired her tenacity and was amazed at how her positive enthusiasm for life always shone through. I was pleased that her relationship with Adrian had developed so well.

Adrian and Ros

While Ros was in the process of trying to settle in Worcestershire and work in Chester she had a bad bout of food poisoning which led to internal bleeding. After some weeks she ended up in MRI for three nights having treatment and a blood transfusion. Adrian was suffering too; his jaw had been accidentally fractured and dislocated playing rugby and he needed corrective surgery, which was ongoing. The blood poisoning incident made Ros decide to transfer her haemophilia care to Queen Elizabeth Hospital (QEH) in Birmingham. She could still be treated at any haemophilia centre, but her day to day care and supplies of treatment could be provided there.

The Haemophilia Society organised a weekend in Sheffield. It was particularly aimed at young people with hepatitis C and their families. The lectures and discussion groups were divided, so that the adults and the young people could talk freely within their own age groups. Adrian was happy to join Ros and us on this weekend. It was a first introduction to the haemophilia world for him and he joined in the discussions with a keen interest. This was so supportive for Ros; I was pleased that Adrian was becoming involved too. He seemed to be taking Ros's health problems in his stride.

While under the care of MRI Ros had never been offered an appointment with a liver specialist. Now she decided that it was time she saw one and this summer she had an appointment with the hepatologist at QEH. We had heard this doctor speak at conferences and we felt sure he would take good care of Ros and her hepatitis. Following blood tests in the autumn he told her that her liver was not too inflamed and that her hepatitis was a genotype that was more responsive to treatment.

One of the best ways of finding out the state of the liver is by a biopsy. There are other procedures in addition to the blood tests – ultrasound, endoscopy and laparoscopy – but a biopsy gives the specialist a sample of the liver to study. The biopsy itself is a straightforward procedure, where a needle is inserted through the skin, under a local anaesthetic and into the liver, to take a sample of tissue. This sample is tested to determine the state of the liver cells. Many of the hepatologists we had heard speak at conferences were reluctant to do biopsies on people with bleeding disorders because of the associated complications. Most people with haemophilia were having their hepatitis C monitored by their centre directors, but one or two we knew had had a biopsy done. A member of the Manor House group had had a biopsy which resulted in very traumatic bleeding. It had been stressed to us often enough that a biopsy would be a bad idea, and we thought that Ros had been likewise persuaded. Knowing her propensity for bleeding, it was obvious to me that it would be a very risky procedure.

Because the interferon had not cleared the hepatitis C, Ros had decisions to make about her future. There was a chance that a second course of treatment with interferon, with the addition of a new drug, ribavirin, could rid her of the virus. Trials of this combination therapy were showing good results. But the big question remained – what was the real state of her liver? Would it be worth the agony of six months of treatment to get rid of this awful virus, or would she be better having a biopsy first to gain a true picture of her state of health? Ros persuaded the liver specialist to do the biopsy.

All through the years of visits to hospitals for treatments and operations, I had had my low times, times when I was so worried about Ros I felt very miserable; times when keeping things going at home was always a struggle and times when I was just too tired to be bothered with anything. But I had never experienced a time when I thought Ros might die. I had always had the utmost faith in the skill of the doctors and nurses to return her to good health after a bleed. A few years earlier, at a conference, Dr Evans asked me, very gently, had I ever thought that Ros might die. My response was that I had never thought that; I had faith in the doctors.

In January 2001 Ros was booked in for her liver biopsy. The hepatologist at QEH was happy to do the biopsy, as he had done a few on other haemophilia patients. On the 29th she phoned us to say that she was going to the hospital that evening in order to secure a bed for the following day, when the biopsy would be done. She was due to stay in for 24 hours after the procedure, to check that her factor VIII back up had worked and that all was well. All along I had worried about her decision, but always Ros said, "I'll be fine, Mother!" She was more concerned about the result of the biopsy than she was about undergoing it. She was used to living with a bleeding disorder, but she was not used to living with hepatitis C.

During the next day I felt restless and miserable. I was thinking of Ros and of the biopsy going ahead and I could not settle to work properly. To add to my unsettled state I read in *The Times* that day that there was a risk to NHS patients, in particular haemophiliacs, who might have contracted vCJD from a blood donor who had died of it. It read, *Scientists were combing hospital records to find how many haemophiliacs were given a clotting agent made from a blood donor in 1996 or 1997 who later learnt that he had vCJD.* We knew very little about the risks of this but had been led to believe that vCJD was unlikely to be transmitted through blood. There had been, as yet, no reported cases of vCJD among the haemophilia community. We kept an open mind, however, after our experience of HCV. It was not the most cheering news of the day.

John and I met in Manchester that evening; he was working as a temporary clerical assistant at the examination board. We had a meal out and went to a concert. There was a message from Adrian on the answerphone when we came home quite late. Ros had had the biopsy at around 4.00pm and was all right when he visited during the evening. We went to bed reassured that all was well.

3.00am and the phone was ringing in our bedroom. John got to it first. His initial sleepy comments made me suspicious as I struggled awake. He handed me the phone. A nurse was phoning from the hospital to say that Ros had developed complications following the biopsy, was in intensive care and was asking for us. I felt the urgency of the situation as I came fully awake. The nurse from the intensive care unit (ICU) slowly repeated the information and said that she thought we should come to the hospital as soon as possible. Adrian had been called and was on his way. Panic was rising in me, more and more as I relayed to John the instructions the nurse was giving me, as to how to find the hospital. We seemed to be on the phone a long time, going over what the situation was and how we would come as quickly as we could. The nurse was thorough, speaking slowly and clearly; she wanted to be sure that we could get there easily and gave us a number to phone in case we got lost. Trying to plan, get dressed and drink a mug of tea all happened within 15 minutes. We scribbled a note for our neighbour, telling her of our sudden disappearance, and pushed it through her letter box. Thankfully there was enough petrol in the car for the journey to Birmingham.

We set off along the motorway in the cold winter morning. The M6 was dark and wet and full of huge black lorries, making the drive like a nightmare. Something serious had happened to Ros and I thought she might die before we could get to her. Both John and I were having the same thought; we even asked each other if we knew what Ros wanted for her funeral arrangements. We had never done that before. It was a ghastly two hours. We found our way through the empty streets of Birmingham to the hospital but could not find the way in. Barriers here and there which did not lift and signs for other departments added to our trauma. In our shocked state we could not make sensible decisions about where to go. I phoned the number the nurse had given us and she got Adrian to phone us and guide us to the entrance, where he waited for us.

In the ICU Ros lay in bed, wired up to so much equipment that we could hardly get near her. She had three lines into her neck, a tube up her nose and a catheter. She was whiter than I had ever seen and very weak. The nurse in charge told us that Ros was in a lot of pain and was suffering from massive internal bleeding in her liver. She was full of morphine but still coherent. There was little that could be done until around 7.30am, when the specialists would arrive and decide what to do. This was still two hours away and I reacted badly, seeing the state Ros was in. I spoke angrily to the staff but realised that I was taking out my anguish and tiredness on them. They were doing the very best they could for Ros. The next few hours were hell; the staff were supportive but it was a busy unit and we could only sit and wait. The specialists duly appeared and had a consultation. They decided they needed to take Ros to theatre and assess the situation via keyhole surgery. Within half an hour Ros was taken down.

John and Adrian went home to get some sleep but I said I would stay at the hospital. I phoned school to tell them where I was and John phoned Veronica, who worked in another department of the exam board. I felt very tired. I was emotionally drained and could not settle at all, not wanting to go far from the unit while Ros was in theatre. I walked to the haemophilia department, which was on the same floor of the hospital, and met the nurse. She sent me to a private room and said she would come along later for a chat. I sat in this bare little room, trying to keep calm. It seemed ages before the haemophilia nurse came, and by then I was in such a state of unease that I just dissolved in tears. There was no news of Ros for some further time. Later I spoke to the haematologist. He was in quite a state too. He could not see what he had done wrong and kept saying so. He had prescribed all the correct factor VIII dosages to keep her clotting levels up and had been sure they were correct. He said, "If anything happens to Ros, I'll resign".

Several hours later Ros was out of theatre and back in ICU. She had had six pints of blood drained from her liver and abdomen. I was very shocked; six pints was an awful lot of blood. It was a very serious situation.

For the rest of the day I sat with Ros; she was drowsy from the anaesthetic and very weak but had less pain, due to the sedation by the morphine. The haematologist came again and we had a chat in the corridor outside. He said that at no time had Ros's life been in danger. I could not agree with him. He was still baffled as to why Ros had bled so badly. I was confused. I had seen Ros bleed internally before but never to this extent, so quickly. I was worried, too, about possible bleeding following the procedures that had been carried out in theatre. Any incision, even a small one, would surely cause additional bleeding.

The only consolation of the day came later, when I spoke to the hepatologist. While in theatre he had been able to see a small section of Ros's liver and in his words, "It looked beautiful". No scarring was apparent.

An extraordinary thing was happening while all this was going on. I had phoned some Quaker friends and told them where I was, asking them for prayerful support for Ros through this crisis. But calls were coming in to the ICU from many of Ros's friends and when the nurse gave her the messages of support, they were from people that she was surprised to hear from. It later transpired that Veronica had phoned Kitty and Kitty had immediately e-mailed a whole list of Ros's contacts, to tell them of the situation. Some were ex-colleagues who did not even know of her bleeding condition, so it must have been a shock. It was good that all those people out there were supporting Ros, thinking of her and hoping for her recovery.

I felt strengthened by Ros herself. When she had been taken to the ICU she had been asked by a nurse who she would like them to contact. Of course she had asked them to phone Adrian first. In her weakened state and in much pain, she could not follow what all the fuss was about, so when she was asked if there was anyone else they could contact she had said, "I suppose you had better phone my

Mum and Dad". John and Adrian came back to see Ros. John drove home to Stockport afterwards and I went back to Worcestershire with Adrian to get some much needed sleep. I was exhausted.

It was a fitful night, sleep coming and going and I woke the next morning feeling tired and depressed. I had brought a few essentials with me, but no change of clothes, so was glad to do some shopping in Kidderminster while Adrian had a physiotherapy appointment. Adrian took me back to the hospital and I spent the rest of the day with Ros. She was still weak and sleepy, but the bleeding seemed to be under control and she was transferred back to the ward during the afternoon. I felt very shocked by the events of the last 36 hours and the specialists still seemed baffled as to what had gone wrong. The doctors ultimately decided that having gone in 'blind' they must have hit the hepatic vein. Since that time, any liver biopsy done on a haemophiliac at QEH is performed with ultrasound support and the doctors use the veins in the neck for entry.

For the next eight days Ros continued to have pain, although she was generally regaining strength. She went home for a weekend but because of continuing discomfort was re-admitted to hospital for observation. It was a regime that she had followed before. Investigations revealed that a large blood clot had formed on her liver and was proving slow to disperse. There was also the possibility of a slow internal bleed occurring elsewhere. She spent a further ten days in hospital. Ros was pale and tired and often in pain, but she cheered up for short periods when visitors came. Back at home she was tired and out of sorts. Her recovery took a further two months and she did not start back at work until the beginning of April.

HCV and Me – An Affair To Forget

You came into my life insidiously.
Like a demon you crawled under my skin,
through my veins and into the heart of me.

Unaware of the danger I plunged on,
not understanding what it was
I was introducing to myself.

You were there
from the very beginning,
intrinsically part of me.

But I knew nothing.
Ignorant of how you were taking over my body,
destroying my soul.

When, later on, I discovered you,
you blew me away.
Turned me upside down
dragged me inside out.
Possessing.
Obsessing.

Flung my life in an unexpected, unbalanced direction.
You exposed my dark and twisted self.
I was never to be the same.

I railed and fought to resist
the all-encompassing nature
of your poison.

Yet you clung to me,
weighing me down,
changing me,
infecting me,
draining me.

Now am I free of you?
Are you gone?
Have you left me, in peace?

Or still dangling,
turning like a body hanging from a tree,
waiting for the wind to pick me up
and play with me once again.

I hate you,
For the gifts you gave me.
The tumultuous emotional tornado,
the paralysing physical pain.

But you made me.
Who I am.
You are still hidden within.

There will always be a fragment of me
devoted to you.

Chapter Fourteen

All this worry and travelling back and forth to the hospital in Birmingham had left me feeling very depressed, weepy and fragile. I was tired all the time and stayed off school, as I knew I could not cope with the stresses there. I had an appointment with a new GP at our practice. He was very understanding, though at first he wanted to tell me all about vWd. (Times had changed. I told him not to bother as I probably knew more than he did!) He arranged for me to have some counselling, which proved helpful over several weeks.

Although I began to feel much better my emotions were taxed again at the Haemophilia Society AGM a few months later. As an introduction to the weekend our president, Lord Alf Morris, addressed the conference. Knowing him to be an active campaigner in the House of Lords for justice for haemophiliacs with HCV, we were always encouraged by him. Now, as he spoke about the misery of HCV, his efforts to get the government to see reason and to pay compensation, I felt totally overwhelmed. Out came my hanky to mop up my tears as I cried all the way through his short address. There was no time to thank this kindly gentleman; he had to leave the conference shortly afterwards.

When Ros had recovered sufficiently from the biopsy to return to work, she was offered the chance of further treatment for her hepatitis C. She felt quite insulted by this. Did the specialists not realise how traumatic the biopsy and its aftermath had been and how much she had suffered? She needed a few months, at least, for some normal life and the opportunity to work to restore herself. She could not face taking treatment that would again leave her feeling ill and keep her off work, so she turned down the offer.

The World Federation of Haemophilia was holding a meeting in Seville in the spring of 2002 and Ros and Adrian went as participants. I was thrilled that Adrian was now so committed to Ros that he wanted to go to such a conference. One evening Ros phoned from Seville. I asked her how the conference was going and she told me something about it, responding to my questions. After quite a chat she said,

"Mum, do you want the other news?" "What other news?" I asked. "Adrian and I are engaged!" she replied. He had proposed to her in Seville, in the throes of a haemophilia conference. How romantic! John and I were overjoyed to hear this news.

Plans for the wedding started but before much had been decided, Ros was again offered the chance of further treatment. This time she decided to go ahead. She knew that her liver was in a reasonable state so the possibility of ridding herself of this terrible virus before the wedding became a high priority.

She started on the six-month long course of injections, interferon with the new drug, ribavirin. The effects were the same as before, knocking her out physically, keeping her off work and leaving her feeling groggy and depressed. The treatment continued through the autumn and winter and she gave herself the final injection early in February. Adrian and two small kittens kept her company and cheered her up throughout this time. In her usual way, she tried hard to keep positive and managed to do a lot of the planning for their autumn wedding while off work. Her morale was given a great boost in June when, following all the blood tests carried out since the end of the treatment, she was pronounced virus free. This was wonderful news!

Prior to the excitement of the wedding we had had another piece of good news. The health secretary, John Reid, announced in August that the government were discussing compensation packages for the thousands of haemophiliacs affected by the hepatitis C virus. Newly appointed in this post John Reid said, "I looked at the history of this issue and decided on compassionate grounds that this is the right thing to do in this situation".

A step forward at last by the government, after all our efforts to make them understand.

Our excitement was soon dampened when we heard how much each recipient might receive – a £20,000 lump sum and a further £25,000 if their illness advanced to a more serious stage. Ros would only be eligible for £20,000 now. She was dismayed when she thought how much loss of earnings she had incurred during all those years out of work. This financial assistance came nowhere near that amount. The terms and conditions of the package were not straightforward and denied many people the right to claim, namely some widows and those who had cleared the virus spontaneously, ie without treatment. Our gratitude for the payment was affected by this. Why should some people get the compensation and others receive nothing? We could not understand the government's attitude. On one hand they seemed to recognise the plight of the haemophilia sufferers, but on the other hand they were not being thorough in their plan. There was no mention of a public inquiry into the whole terrible tragedy.

It was September 2003. The wedding day came. What a wonderful day it was. Even the weather was kind! With their families and friends around them, Adrian and Ros were married in a small country church at Rushock in Worcestershire. The church was beautifully decorated with calla lilies and deep red flowers, with arrangements on the end of the pews. Ros wore a slim fitting ivory dress with a small train, the bodice adorned with tiny jewels. A sequinned veil was held by a small tiara and she carried a bouquet of blood red roses. She looked stunning. Kitty and Karen were her two bridesmaids, wearing dresses of deep red silk.

The service was led by a vicar well-known to Adrian's family. Ros's friend, Louise, gave one of the readings. My brother, Nick, introduced a few minutes of silence for quiet thought and for ministry from any of the congregation, to reflect Ros's Quaker background. My brother, Ben, spoke about finding periods of quiet in our lives. He hoped that Ros and Ade could just be quiet together sometimes, and perhaps find something rich and enduring by doing so. After a short pause, Kitty spoke, giving thanks for Ros and Ade, truly wonderful friends and wished them a long and happy journey through life. It was a day to remember for so much happiness was there, tinged with sadness for those who were absent. I particularly remembered Ros's birth mother and spoke briefly about her during this silent time. I then read from the Quaker guidelines, *Advices and Queries: Marriage has always been regarded by Friends as a religious commitment rather than a merely civil contract. Both partners should offer with God's help an intention to cherish one another for life. Remember that happiness depends on an understanding and steadfast love on both sides. In times of difficulty remind yourself of the value of prayer, of*

Wedding group
l-r: John, Juliet, Ros, Adrian, Maureen

Wedding group
l-r: Karen, Ros, Paul, Kitty, David

perseverance and a sense of humour.

Ros's cousin, Caroline, played her violin from the gallery of the church during the signing of the registers. Ros hobbled slowly and happily down the aisle, on the arm of her new husband, smiling broadly and greeting everyone. The reception was held at the Hilton hotel at Bromsgrove where Caroline's sister, Beth, welcomed us, playing popular tunes on the grand piano.

In his speech at the reception, John spoke about Ros's wicked sense of humour. Unaware that some people attending the reception did not know of Ros's condition, John said, "If you've got haemophilia you need a sense of humour to cope with it". With a huge smile on his face, he shared this anecdote from the early days when Ros was about three. He said he had felt a duty to try and educate her, so one day, when out on a walk, this conversation took place:

John: "Look Rosamund, can you see that robin over there?"
Rosamund: "No".
John: "Oh surely you can see that robin over on that tree?"
Rosamund: No response
John: "I look down. She's got her eyes screwed tight and a broad smile on her face!"

The wonderful day that Ros had always longed for came to its end in the small hours of the following morning. What a lovely day it had been.

Excerpt from Ros's blog, 5 August 2010

Foibilicious
If you know me, you'll be aware that I have a number of foibles, slight peculiarities, idiosyncrasies, eccentricities. I believe they are worth celebrating.

- *talking to myself - I do this all the time, because I spend a lot of time alone perhap?? Weirdly I catch myself doing it without even realising - usually in the supermarket or wandering down the street. Then I tell myself off. Out loud.*
- *talking to inanimate objects - I talk to the trees, but they do not listen to me. No really, I do talk to things - vegetables, furniture, plants, doors, taps, bits of my body. Maybe I enjoy not getting a response.*
- *sound effects - I provide sound effects. Why? No idea. Didn't even know I did it until a friend at work pointed it out one day. Then realised I do it all the blooming time. If a door creaks I'll do a creaky noise. If driving round a bend I'll emit a skidding sound effect. If driving a shopping trolley around a corner I'll do the same. If I see a ball bounce I'll produce a boing.*
- *talking for things - I not only talk to the animals, but for them as well. I must have watched too much Johnny Morris as a child because if I see an animal - a cat on a street, a goose in a field, a duck on a river - I talk to them and then I reply for them, with appropriate animal / bird voice. I can have quite a splendid little conversation this way.*
- *talking for babies - I also cannot help but do this for babies too. If a baby's playing with something I will provide a commentary - what I imagine baby to be thinking. I guess what they would say when they look at you askance (which is probably because you are having a conversation with yourself). I can't help myself and enjoy trying to figure out what they might say if only they could. Probably irritating as hell for the parents. I think this stems from at the age of 6 wishing I could do the voices for Count Duckula or Mighty Mouse.* (Author's note: I still have a cassette recording we did of Ros, aged 8, reading The Enormous Crocodile by Roald Dahl, with all the voices!)
- *silliness - no explanation needed here, think the foibles above are testament to this. I am a silly billy and I am not ashamed.*
- *word play - I like to make new words. Taking existing words and changing them a little. For instance Foibilicious. Can't think of any more at the moment but I know there are squillions.*

Epilogue

For me, writing about Ros's health problems has been thought-provoking. My life changed on meeting Ros. She was a much longed for baby, then came all the problems attached to her arrival, once her bleeding disorder was diagnosed. Particular incidents stick in my mind, for example Bristol Children's Hospital in the early days and the more recent biopsy in Birmingham. Even now I react fearfully when the phone rings in the middle of the night. To me it is always going to be bad news. And how often have I sat and watched the slow drip of a fluid through a plastic tube into Ros's vein, a saline drip or a blood transfusion, one drop slowly following another, hour after hour. In the past I never thought much about where the blood came from – it was just supplied to help Ros. Enormous thanks must go to all the blood donors who have helped restore her to health after a major bleed. I am sure that the anxiety of living with someone with a bleeding disorder often outweighs the problems actually incurred by the sufferer.

Through telling Ros's story I hope I have put into perspective how information on bleeding disorders is more available. So much progress has been made since the 1970's. A bleeding condition be it haemophilia, von Willebrands or Christmas disease, is still a hidden condition. These days, children are treated with recombinant factor VIII and prophylactic treatment. They can lead much more normal lives than those who suffered forty years ago. At a Haemophilia Society AGM and family weekend a few years back, I watched the children walking through the hotel foyer to go on their coach outing. Not one of them limped or walked with a crutch, no one was in a wheel chair. It was impossible to pick out which of them suffered from a bleeding disorder.

Von Willebrand's type 3 has an incidence of one in a million. How Ros has coped so brilliantly with it all her life is quite amazing. It is her strength and determination to carry on and lead a normal life, coupled with her calm disposition and a sense of humour that have carried her so far already. How often have I heard her say that there is someone worse off than her. She has helped me to live through many a rough patch and she is always willing to help her many friends where she can. I can safely say that Ros is "one in a million"!

Appendix 1 – full text of letter from Chapter 3

"As you will appreciate, there are numerous problems to be overcome but this in no way reduces our concern to see that the difficulties which your constituents are facing are kept to the absolute minimum.

I have been advised by an expert group which has been studying this subject that it is necessary to process the plasma from about 350,000 blood donations annually to produce sufficient factor VIII for the treatment of patients suffering from haemophilia and similar disorders in this country. Factor VIII is available either in the form of a preparation known as cryoprecipitate or in the form of anti-haemophilic globulin (AHG) concentrate, also known as 'freeze dried' factor VIII concentrate. On the present basis the plasma from some 75,000 donations would be used to provide cryoprecipitate but the greater part, from approximately 275,000 donations, would be used to provide AHG concentrate. I understand that at this level of production factor VIII could also be made available to haemophiliacs for whom treatment outside hospital can be recommended.

Factor VIII in the form of cryoprecipitate can usually be supplied in sufficient quantities to meet requirements, although local shortages do occasionally occur but, as Mr and Mrs Batten suggest, there is an immediate need to provide more AHG concentrate. At present, part of the demand for this material is being met by imported products, but these are expensive and health authorities feel they cannot afford to buy as much as they would wish. It has been estimated that it would cost about £2 million a year to treat haemophilic patients in this country with AHG concentrate purchased from commercial firms. Purchases by health authorities are running at the rate of slightly over £1/2 million a year, but we have to face the fact that this is one of the many costly treatments and other aspects of patient care are competing for priority.

However, I regard it as most important that the National Health Service should become self-sufficient as soon as practicable in the production of AHG concentrate. That is why I have authorised the allocation of special finance of up to £1/2 million to boost our own production of this material, mainly through the installation of additional facilities. To achieve our objective we shall also need the full cooperation of all clinicians who, by using for transfusions considerably more concentrated red cells rather than whole blood, can free extra plasma for conversion into AHG concentrate.

Production within the National Health Service of AHG concentrate during the first nine months of 1975 was some 15% up in comparison with the corresponding period last year. Of course production is still far short of what is needed, but it is as yet too early to see any results from the extra money. The arrangements which we had to make to use this money efficiently were complex and have taken some time to carry through and I have never expected that the first effects would be felt much before the end of this year. In the light of estimates which have recently been made by Regional Health Authorities I hope that in about a year we will be able to meet some two-thirds of the present requirements for AHG concentrate and that within two years we may be able to reach the target which we have set ourselves. I appreciate that this may not be regarded as soon enough by Mr and Mrs Batten, but health authorities are free to purchase additional supplies of AHG concentrate from commercial firms when they consider that it is right to do so. With medical advice they can best judge the individual cases and balance the needs, taking into account the many demands on their limited resources."

Happy Ending?

Find out how Ros is now by reading her blog.

http://rosamundcooper.blogspot.com

Useful addresses:

The Haemophilia Society
1st Floor, Petersham House,
57a, Hatton Garden,
London EC1N 8JG
Tel: 020 7831 1020
www.haemophilia.org.uk

Adoption UK
Linden House,
55, The Green,
South Bar Street,
Banbury OX16 9AB
Tel: 01295 752240
www.adoptionuk.org

www.mygirlsblood.org

www.womenbleedtoo.org.uk/index.php?pub_content_id=3